by Russell Davis and Brent Ashabranner

The Lion's Whiskers
Point Four Assignment
Ten Thousand Desert Swords

TEN THOUSAND DESERT SWORDS

illustrated by
LEONARD EVERETT FISHER

Little, Brown and Company

TEN THOUSAND DESERT SWORDS

The Epic Story
of a Great Bedouin Tribe

by
Russell Davis
and Brent Ashabranner

Boston   Toronto

LIBRARY OF CONGRESS CATALOG CARD NO. 60–9336

FIRST EDITION

Published simultaneously in Canada
by Little, Brown & Company (Canada) Limited

PRINTED IN THE UNITED STATES OF AMERICA

To Cindy and Melissa

Contents

THE SONS OF HILAL: FACT AND LEGEND

This book is about a great tribe of desert warriors known as Bani Hilal, which means "the Sons of Hilal." The Bani Hilal do not exist today, but a thousand years ago they formed one of the most powerful Arab tribes. They were a rough Bedouin people, and in the pre-Islamic age they roamed throughout ancient Arabia, Iraq, and Syria. They were constantly on the move, looking for grass and water for their great herds of camels and horses. In times of drought and famine, they lived by their swords, and the name of Bani Hilal was feared throughout the Arab world.

When Islam was born, the Sons of Hilal adopted the new religion and became conquerors in the name of the Prophet Mohammed. They overran Egypt on the eastern side of the Nile and then invaded the North African countries that today are called Libya and Tunisia. When there were no enemy tribes to fight, the fierce and restless Bani Hilal fought among themselves, "like fire which eats itself when there is nothing else to eat." But in the end, it was soft and easy living in the cities of Tunisia that caused the breakdown of this powerful tribe.

The few facts above are all that is known about the Sons of Hilal; and had it not been for Ibn Kaldum, the great Arab historian, we would not know even this much of actual fact. Yet today, hundreds of years after the disappearance of the tribe, the name of Bani Hilal is well known to almost every Arab in the Middle East. The reason for this is that the deeds of the Sons of Hilal have lived on in story, song, and poetry.

The legends of the tribe are known from Spain to Indonesia, wherever Arabs, the Arabic language, and the Moslem religion have gone. The beggar in Rabat, the goatherd in the Fezzan, the urchin and nobleman in Damascus, the sailor in Massawa, the Holy Man in the Sind Province of Pakistan, all can sing of the Hilalies. In the coffee houses of Amman today professional storytellers chant the marvelous legends of Bani Hilal to eager listeners. A skillful narrator ends each day's story at some exciting point so that his audience will come back the next day, and he can stretch out the Hilal legends so that it takes him a whole year to tell them. The Jordanian army still hires minstrels to sing to the troops about the brave deeds of Bani Hilal.

In legend, no tribe was as great as the Sons of Hilal. A half million was the number of their horses and camels. They lived near the mighty well, Bir Jaufa, where from fifty openings in the earth, water gushed in bountiful streams. Abu Zaid was the greatest Hilal warrior; protected by jinn, he could not be harmed by sword, spear, or arrow. Diab ben Gannim was the second greatest warrior and hunter of the Hilal. His spear, once thrown, was fated always to strike flesh and bone. Emir Hassan ruled the Bani Hilal. Budair was their all-wise judge. No women were more beautiful than the women of Bani Hilal; and Jazieh, sister of Hassan, was the most beautiful of all. The enemies of the Hilalies — the Fire Worshipers, Zenaiti the Wicked, Alan the Slave who killed with a great iron hook, the Fana Whirlwind — were the most wicked and fierce enemies of the world of legend.

The legends of Bani Hilal form one of the great epics of Arabic folk literature. Not only are they exciting, colorful stories, but they give an excellent picture of Bedouin life, customs and beliefs. Anyone who knows the legends of Bani Hilal will find it easier to understand the modern Arab world. Though customs have changed through the years there are still some beliefs, values, and traditions that are unchanging. The Arab's admiration for generosity and hospitality, his fondness for things of beauty, be it poetry, horses or women, his pride and courage and loyalty to his tribe and his willingness to take long chances for no material gain — all of these are still important for the best of the modern Arabs.

It is a puzzling fact that the legends of Bani Hilal are almost unknown outside of the Moslem world. The stories have never been told in English except for sketchy and incomplete summaries in one or two scholarly books on Arabic life and literature. To our knowledge, *Ten Thousand Desert Swords* is the first book in any language other than Arabic to be devoted entirely to capturing the spirit and substance of the stories of the Sons of Hilal.

We have not tried to tell all of the stories, for to do so would require a book of many hundreds of pages. We have chosen to tell those tales which seemed to us best and most representative of the whole epic. We do not apologize for the great amount of action and fighting in the stories. To eliminate these would be to destroy the character of the legends and of the Sons of Hilal themselves, who were a proud, aggressive, fighting people.

RUSSELL DAVIS
BRENT ASHABRANNER

TEN THOUSAND DESERT SWORDS

BANI HILAL: A TRIBE IS BORN

At that time the number of the tribe of Hilal was one. He lived alone on the sands to the west of Kaba near Jabal Subh (the Morning Mountain). One day this boy would become Abu Hilal, father of the thousands of sons of Hilal, but in the beginning he was one, and alone. At that time, too, the land was not as it is now. Most of the land was robed in green forests and meadows and belted with blue rivers. There was only one small quarter of empty sands, to the west of Jabal Subh. There, the one Hilal had been driven because he was only one, without family or tribesmen. He wandered alone, without horse or camel, and without mother or father, sister or brother.

He lived because he grew swift enough to chase and catch the desert gazelle. He lived because he grew wise enough to snare the hen of the desert and catch water from the heavens, cunning enough to take eggs from the nests of mountain birds, brave and strong enough to battle hungry wolves for his food. But strength and swiftness and wisdom and bravery do not make a man a family out of sand and rock and wild beasts. He longed for a mother and father when he was young, and a wife and child when he grew older.

Because he had neither family nor kinsmen he looked often toward the heavens, for the stars were bright and clear above the sands. In the stars he found that he could create people. He made points of the stars and by joining these points he created shapes. Out of these shapes he created in the sky, mother and father, brother and sister. He had only to turn his head this way or that or cover one eye with his hand or twist his body, and he could make his family move in the heavens.

So he was never lonely out on the sands. He took his food. He caught rain water from the heavens and stored it in a stone pit on the mountainside. He had his family in heaven. The years passed.

One cold night he woke and, as was his custom, stared up at the heavens. He found his mother and father, now old and withered, and his brothers, larger and stronger. Some of his sisters were missing. They had gone to live with men in other tribes. And without his trying to see it, there was another face and figure in the starry heaven. It was a woman. He did not have to twist his head or strain his eyes to see her. Her face and figure shone clearly in the stars. Her face glowed as none of the

others did, for it was made of the brightest stars. He could not
turn his head in any way without seeing her. He stared up at
her, and his sighs made white puffs in the cold air. He watched
her until dawn. She disappeared only when the star of morning
was brighter than all others.

On the next night he again watched the woman in the heavens. Her radiance made all of the other figures seem dim. As he
watched her face through drifting clouds, it seemed that she
smiled down on him.

Each night he stared up at her and she looked down at him.
Her eyes reflected his sorrow and his joy. When the day had
been good, when rain had fallen or he had killed a fat desert
gazelle, her eyes sparkled with happiness. When the day had
been bad, and the fire saw no meat, her eyes were clouded over
and dim. She shared his joys and sorrows. She was the most
faithful, with him in summer and in winter.

Still, she was very far away. He was on the cold sand alone,
and she was in the high heavens. "Send her to me," he begged
the desert night. "Send her down to me."

And one night a star slipped away from her shape and fell
toward earth trailing fire. Then she was no more. The pattern
was gone. Try as he might, he could see her no longer in the
heaven. He knew that his plea had been answered. She had
come down to earth. He marked the direction in which the star
had fallen. It was to the east across the hills toward the lands of
the great tribes.

He traveled east in the morning, and from the start his journey went well. There was game on the plains and in the hills. Water fell from the sky during the night. He traveled day and night. He did not look up at the heavens in the night, for he knew she was no longer there. She was on the earth somewhere.

In the high hills it was cold, but the thought of his goal warmed him. He made a covering for his back out of the skins of the gazelle, and he made wrappings for his feet to protect them from the cruel rocks of the mountains. He crossed the mountains, and on the other side, for the first time that he could remember, he saw green country.

He traveled into the green country by night, and when day came, he could tell by the crowing of some strange bird that he was in the land of a strange tribe. He slept through most of the day in a deep clump of trees, and in the late afternoon when animals would be going to water, he crept forth to hunt. He went through the forest and came out on the bank of a pool. Never had he seen so much water in one pool. Try as he might, he could not see to the bottom of that pool. He drank from the sweet water of the pool until his head spun; then, hearing the noise of many feet, he hid himself in some reeds at the edge of the pool.

The footsteps were those of animals he had never seen before. First there were small animals with short horns and chin whiskers. Then there were animals with a thick woolly covering of dark gray. Then there were tall, dun-colored animals, the color of desert sand, and with humps on their backs. And there

were fat animals with wide-spread horns. He watched them in wonder.

And in the midst of the animals was the woman he sought. She looked little different when walking the earth than she had when smiling down from the sky. She was alone. He stood up in the reeds. When she saw him, she gave no cry.

"I have come for you," he said. "Come!"

She walked around the pool and stood before him. He walked

all around her because he had only seen one side of her from where he lay on earth. Her eyes were just as bright as he remembered them. Her form was just as perfect.

"My name is Nijmeh," she said.

"I know," he answered, because the name means *star*. He said, "I am Hilal."

She nodded. He began to lead her away from the pool. Though he knew she was his, fallen from heaven to be his alone, he was in the country of enemies, and he had to be quickly gone.

She twisted away from him suddenly and ran splashing back to the other side of the pool. But he was not afraid she would run away. He did not call to her. He waited, and she picked a pair of each of the animals and drove them across to him. She was not coming without a dowry.

They traveled by day toward the western mountains and hid in forests at night. A *gom* (raiding party) of the enemy tribe followed them. Often in the night fierce riders of the *gom* came within yards of where Hilal lay hidden. But the girl and the animals made no sound. After three days, there was no sound of the *gom,* and Hilal and Nijmeh were in the foothills of the western mountains.

On the next day they crossed the mountain and looked down on the empty sands of his home. When she saw the empty dunes the girl cried out.

"Be not afraid," he told her. "This is my home. Nothing can hurt you here. There is food and water."

"I cannot believe that anything lives in such a waste," Nijmeh told him. "We can not live there, surely. What of water?"

"There is water enough for both of us," he told her. "I catch the water from the heavens. We will found a great tribe on those sands. They will be the Sons of Hilal."

"Never," she said. "We can never do such a thing until there is water." She nodded toward the animals. The furry one and the one with short horns were lying on the edge of the sand. "They can go no farther without water," she told him. "Even the camels will not live long without it."

"We will drink from my pool," he told her.

Together they carried the small animals through the broken rocks toward Hilal's pool. But when they got there, Hilal was amazed and the woman Nijmeh overcome with grief. For the pool — which had seemed wide and deep to Hilal — now seemed only a tiny puddle. And when he drank of the water it was not sweet.

Nijmeh drank and cried, "Oh! This is bad water. And so little of it. How will we live! Our animals will drink it dry this night."

"Kill the animals then," Hilal told her.

"Never. If we do, we are no more than animals ourselves. We must find water for them, or there will be no Sons of Hilal."

"Very well," Hilal agreed. "I will look for it." So he set off into the desert. He took no water because there was little in the pool.

The sun stood high and hot in the heavens. All the brown

dunes wavered in the light, as Hilal walked across the desert searching for water. But there was nothing green as far as the eye could see. He plodded up dunes and down into *wadis,* and finally his feet burned so that he could scarcely walk. He did not know where to look for water in the great sands. Never before had he needed water. Always, the rain had furnished enough for him. But now with the woman and the animals he needed more than the winter rains would bring.

He went on across the sands, sometimes slipping and falling. At times he reached the top of a dune only by clawing with hands and walking on his knees. He grew weak. The sun bleached the color out of his eyes. His face burned and cracked. But he went on. He thought that he might die, but he knew he would never stop until he died or found water.

He reached the top of a huge dune. He was crawling on his stomach and leaving the mark of a snake in the sand. And then he could crawl no more. He pitched forward and rolled down the edge of the dune. He rolled and the sand flew and he felt that he was rolling to his death. But when he stopped rolling, he lay at the edge of a great pool.

The water in the pool stretched as far as his half-blind eyes could see. The edges of the pool were smooth and round. It was as though something had fallen straight down from above and made a perfectly round hole in the desert sand. The hole was not old, for no trees or shrubs grew near the edge of the pool. There were no rushes or reeds. Hilal drank and bathed and set off back to get Nijmeh and the animals.

Great was Nijmeh's joy when she saw the pool in the desert. "This will serve us," she said. "Soon the edges of the pool will be green. This is a gift from heaven. The pool was made by a falling star. The sons of Hilal will be many."

And this was so. Wherever Hilal stuck a stick in the ground new water came. The plain round about the pool became covered with greenery, camels, the sons of Hilal, and the many wells of Bir Jaufa. For each son of Abu Hilal, a new well appeared in the desert.

2

FATHER FIGHTS SON IN THE TRIBE OF HILAL

Abu Hilal had a favorite son whose name was Munthir. Munthir was born when Abu Hilal was old, when the tribe was rich, and when Abu Hilal's other sons, their wives and their kinsmen had made the tribe of Hilal many and strong. Though Abu Hilal had many sons and grandsons, Munthir was his favorite. Abu Hilal denied nothing to Munthir. Since Munthir got everything he wanted, he grew in time to expect everything.

One day in the market of a coastal town, Munthir saw a beautiful girl who walked with the grace of raindrops crossing quiet water. Watching her, Munthir loved her, and he sent his old sword-bearer to find out the tribe she belonged to.

The sword-bearer inquired through the market. When he returned he said sadly to Munthir, "Woe. The girl you ask of is Hasna, daughter of the chief of the Bani Uniza."

Hearing this, Munthir struck himself a blow on the face. "Why!" he cried. "Why should this be so? The Bani Uniza are enemies of the Bani Hilal. Her father is my father's enemy. Woe!"

The sword-bearer, who was like a father to Prince Munthir, said, "Think no more of it. Soon we will be riding against the Uniza. Perhaps you can capture the woman and take her as a slave."

"I want her as my wife," Munthir said. "If I take her as a slave she will be only a slave."

"There is one other thing," the sword-bearer said. "I must also tell you — "

" I do not care to hear it," Munthir said. "I will talk to Budair."

Munthir went to the chambers of Budair, a great and wise judge of Bani Hilal. To Budair, Munthir said, "I wish to take as wife a woman who is of the tribe of Uniza. How shall I approach my father about this?"

"There is no way," Budair told him.

"But he has never denied me anything before," said Munthir. "Why should he deny me this?"

"Because this matters not to your father as a father," Budair told him. "This matters to your father as chief of the Bani Hilal. He must refuse you. A marriage to a daughter of Abu Uniza is impossible at this time."

Munthir dashed straightway to the tent of Abu Hilal, his father. He pushed his way inside even though the oldest men of the tribe were there, and he said, "Father, I am in love with a daughter of the Uniza. I must take her to wife."

Abu Hilal was angry because his son had interrupted an important council meeting. "Do you not see these graybeards of our tribe in solemn council?" he asked. "What madness is this? Even as a prince of the Bani Hilal you have no right to blurt your personal business at a time like this. Out!"

Munthir had no choice but to leave the tent in disgrace. But he waited outside, hidden behind a bush. When the council meeting was over, two chiefs of the Hilalies passed near Munthir's hiding place. One of them said, "The council meeting was long. But the sand has been cut, and the decision made. We must avenge the blood insult given us by the tribe of Uniza."

Munthir knew then that he had no chance. The council had been meeting to decide on a war against the Unizas. Abu Hilal would never share food or a wedding feast with Abu Uniza. All was lost. Yet Munthir was determined to ask his father just the same.

When Munthir came before his father, his father was already busy preparing for war against the Bani Uniza. Messengers were being sent out to distant kinsmen. Cattle, goats, camels and horses were being brought back across the Wadi L-Ula where they would be safe from the *gom* of the Uniza. Swords had to be sharpened and spears pointed. Abu Hilal listened to his son's plea and said: "There can be no marriage to an enemy."

Munthir would not listen to reason. He became terribly angry. "Very well," he shouted, "but do not expect me and my friends to fight against the Unizas."

Munthir at once gathered all of the servants and soldiers who were attached to the princely guard. He persuaded all of his young friends to follow him out of the lands of Hilal. The old sword-bearer said, "It is my duty to go. But you should know — "

But Munthir would not listen to him. "I need no advice," Munthir answered. "I take with me the best of the young Hilalies. My father will feel the weight of our *gom*. We will fight for the Unizas."

Saying this, Munthir led his men out of the land of Bani Hilal. They rode deep into the Nejd toward the camp of the Unizas. Spies had already warned the Unizas that the Hilalies were going to attack them. From a mountain peak the scouts of the Unizas saw Munthir's band coming toward their land. The word was passed, "The Hilalies are attacking."

Abed, greatest warrior of Bani Uniza, gathered the fighting men of the tribe. Abed himself was preparing for his wedding with Princess Hasna. But preparations for the wedding feast were stopped. The Hilalies had to be beaten first. Abed spoke to his men:

"The Hilalies are led by young Munthir. Nowhere in the *gom* is the old wolf, his father. Perhaps even now he and his band are in the hills waiting for us to move against the boy. But this we will not do. The boy is a decoy. Let the *gom* of

Munthir come into our land, but station two parties of horse-men in the hills that surround the valley of Ranya. When Mun-thir and his men come out of the valley, we can strike from two directions. By then we may know where the old wolf and his pack are waiting."

Munthir and his men rode on into the land of Bani Uniza. They knew by now that scouts must have seen them approach-ing. Yet the Unizas did not attack. "They know that we come here in peace," Munthir said. "They have heard that we have left the Bani Hilal."

Munthir and his men entered the valley of Ranya. From the hills on the right side of Ranya, Abed and his men watched. They exchanged signals with the party in the opposite hills. Abed, old and disfigured by wounds, looked down on the bright face of young Munthir. "See how bravely he rides," Abed said. "I wish that he were my son."

Abed's only son had been killed in a raid the year before. For one year Abed had grieved. An old raider, who had ridden long with Abed, knew of his sorrow. "Be happy," he said. "Soon Hasna will bear you many sons."

"That is so," Abed agreed. "We must have done with this fight so the wedding can go on. But this is a fine prince who rides below. I am glad that I myself will not have to kill him."

At that moment a rider who had been sent to scout to the east rode up to Abed. "I have found the *gom* of old Abu Hilal. It is still beyond the Wadi L-Ula. It has not left the territory of Bani Hilal."

"How strange," Abed said. "So the old one sends his son alone against us. Then this one must be as great in war as he is handsome in appearance. I will have to kill him myself. Let us strike when they reach the end of the valley."

Munthir was now riding toward the place where the valley of Ranya ended at a *wadi,* and the plain of the Unizas began. "It is strange they have not hailed us," he said to his companions. "They must know we are in their land. This proves that the Unizas are our friends. All of this trouble is the doing of old men."

Munthir's party reached the end of the valley, and at that moment the Uniza warriors from the left charged down with mighty cries. Munthir and his men wheeled to meet them. At the same time, Abed and his men charged from the right with even louder shouts.

It would have gone badly for Munthir's men had it not been for the old sword-bearer. He knew better than to fight on two sides. When the second party charged, the sword-bearer hit Munthir's horse a great slap with the flat of the sword. The horse bolted forward across a river and onto the open plain. All of Munthir's men followed, and for the moment they were free of the trap.

Beyond the river, they wheeled and began to fight. They were the youngest and strongest of the Hilalies and they fought well. Blood sparkled where the river ran fast and made dark pools where it ran slow.

As Abed watched Munthir's men charge out of the trap, he

said, "As I thought. This prince is a great warrior. I myself must kill him, or we may lose this battle."

Abed and his guard of old soldiers swinging their square swords hacked their way through Munthir's men and reached the opposite bank of the river. When he saw Abed approach, Munthir was afraid. It was his first battle and already he faced the greatest warrior of the Unizas. He cried out, "Deliver me! We come as friends."

Because Munthir cried out in the din of battle no one but

his sword-bearer heard him. The old sword-bearer had never surrendered, and he had no wish to have his prince turn coward before the Unizas. He called to Munthir:

"Here comes Abed. I have tried to tell you before that Hasna is promised to him. He is the warrior to whom Hasna will be married. Foolish boy. He will offer your head to her father as a wedding payment. How fine will you seem to her then?"

Munthir was so enraged at his sword-bearer that he tried to ride him down. "That is not true," he shouted. "He is old. She is young."

"He is old, but he has no sons. She will bear him sons."

Abed and his ferocious guards had almost reached Munthir and his guard. The blade of Abed's swinging sword made a second shining river in the sunlight. The men of Hilal were swept away. Munthir, thinking only of Hasna, called, "Oh, Abed, is it true that you will marry Hasna, the princess?"

"As soon as I have your head, noble prince," Abed answered.

"That you will never have," Munthir shouted. He spurred his horse forward, swept under the arc of the great swinging sword, and killed Abed with one thrust of his javelin.

When the Unizas saw that their hero was dead, they began to pull back across the river. Munthir's men attacked them in the river and routed them. The Unizas were driven out across the plain toward their camp. Munthir's warriors would have pursued them, but they were too few.

"Let us return to Bani Hilal," Munthir said. "We have

proved ourselves fighters. We have earned the right to sit in the highest councils of Hilal. There will be peace with the Unizas now, and I will marry Hasna."

But the elders of Bani Hilal would not listen to Munthir and his men. "You have disgraced us," they said. "You went as traitors to the land of Bani Uniza and mere luck guided you. Should traitors be rewarded? No. Instead, your fathers should punish you."

Even after the *gom* of the older Hilalies had raided into the land of the Unizas and beaten the rest of their army, the elders refused to honor Munthir and his young warriors. Munthir again went before his father. "I ask of you a share of the spoils of battle, for my men and I made your victory possible. And there is one thing above all that I ask — I wish to marry Hasna."

Abu Hilal's eyes were sad as he spoke. "That cannot be. Hasna was taken in the raid."

"Then I will have her. Who has her?"

"She is no more," Abu Hilal said. "When we captured her she was dead in spirit. She grieved greatly because her hero Abed had been slain. On the second night of our return march she had a faithful slave kill her. I cannot give her to you."

"I do not believe it," Munthir said angrily. "She would not have grieved over such an ugly one as Abed. She is held by one of the Hilalies."

"Do you accuse me of lying?"

"Someone lies," shouted Munthir.

Abu Hilal arose. "Be gone from my sight," he said sternly. "And you shall have nothing from the Bani Uniza raids."

Budair tried to bring peace between Abu Hilal and Munthir, but nothing could be done. Father and son were cut from the same mountain. Munthir turned from his father's tent and called the young men of Bani Hilal together.

"The victory over the Unizas belongs to us," he said, "yet we are given nothing. I say let us look out for ourselves. Who will follow me?"

Many young men who had not joined Munthir the first time, now came to his side. They knew of the victory over Abed at the river and wished to serve a great leader. But the old sword-bearer did not join him.

"I rode with you before because it was my duty," he said. "But the Hilalies are my people. This is my home. I cannot go out to live as a hunted animal."

Munthir was sad that his sword-bearer would not come with him. But he was young, and already he had forgotten what the sword-bearer had done for him at the river. So Munthir and his men rode away again. Henceforth they would turn their hands against all tribes, even the Bani Hilal.

Munthir and his followers settled in a deep valley in the mountains. They had no camels, cattle, or horses. They had no women. They had to take everything from other tribes. They raided north, east, south and west, throughout the Nejd and throughout Arabia. They were great on horse and in battle, and each day Munthir's skill and cunning grew. They had no need to raid against the Bani Hilal, but Munthir enjoyed raids against them most of all.

Some of his men counseled him against raiding the Hilalies. "They are our kinsmen," they said.

"They have done us injury," Munthir answered. "We will ride against them as against all other tribes."

Meanwhile, among the Bani Hilal chieftains, murmuring began. At first the tribe had allowed Munthir's raiders to take their pick of the flock. Many of the Hilalies felt that Munthir's men had deserved a share from the conquest of the Unizas. But soon Munthir's *gom* had taken far more than had been won from the Unizas. Hilali warriors gathered outside Abu Hilal's tent.

"We must crush Munthir," they said. "We must crush him or he will destroy us."

At first Abu Hilal ignored those who protested, for he could not forget that Munthir was his son. But the protests against Munthir grew each day. Poets sang of the break between father and son. Many hearts overflowed with hatred.

At last Abu Hilal said, "I will write to my son. He is older and wiser now. He will listen."

So Abu Hilal wrote a kind letter to his son. But the raids continued. "Perhaps he did not receive the letter," Abu Hilal said. "Perhaps evil counselors kept it from him. I will write again."

So Abu Hilal wrote a second letter to Munthir. There was no answer to the second letter, and the raids grew worse. The daughter of a great chieftain was taken. The camels of rich and good men were driven off.

"I will write one more letter to him," Abu Hilal said. "Surely this will bring him to his senses. I will write him a stern letter."

When Munthir read the third letter he called a council of his bravest young men. "So," Munthir said, "my father now threatens us."

In front of all of his men, Munthir called the messenger and forced him to kneel at his feet. The messenger, who was a noble old Hilali, muttered in his thick beard, but he knelt.

"Take this letter back to my father," Munthir ordered the messenger. "Tell him that it is written wrong. It begins, *My beloved son* and is signed *Your Father, Emir Hilal.* It should have begun, *Honorable Emir Munthir, Prince of all good Hilalies.*"

When the messenger reported how Munthir had treated him, and when he repeated Munthir's proud words, Abu Hilal spoke, "He who bears my son a grudge may fight him. Go with my blessing."

The Bani Hilal again prepared for war. The forces of Hilal attacked Munthir when he and his band were returning from a raid. They attacked Munthir on the mountainside, and because his men were weary from a long march they were driven down into their deep valley. They fought desperately, but the strong forces of Hilal were too much for them. When night fell only Munthir and ten of his men were able to escape into the mountains.

From the mountains Munthir sent a letter to his father, asking for peace. When Abu Hilal read the letter, he shook his head sadly. "Tell your outlaw chief that this is written wrong," he said to Munthir's messenger. "It is addressed *Dear Father* and signed *Your son, Munthir*. I no longer have a son Munthir. But you may tell the outlaw Munthir that there can be no pardon when blood has been shed."

When Munthir heard of his father's answer he knew that there was no place near the land of Bani Hilal where he could lay his head.

"Curse my father," Munthir cried. "He drives me out into the desert to die."

Munthir traveled through the Land of Great Sands toward the eastern sea. Since no man could travel through the lands of the wild Badu with so small a party, Munthir had to fight his way through. He and his ten men sold their services as warriors to many desert chieftains. After he had fought for each chief a while, Munthir and his men moved on toward the east protected by his former chief. At last Munthir reached the domain of the Emir of Uman. Munthir and his men joined the army of the emir.

Fighting for the Emir of Uman, Munthir proved himself a great warrior. He had no other life but the raid and the war. He traveled across the desert, riding day and night. Since he was sad, he seldom slept, and he stood all of the night watches. His *gom* were never ambushed or trapped. Whenever there was a fight, Munthir rushed to the middle of it. And Munthir learned every path and trail and rock and *wadi* of the country around

Uman. But still he was always sad, for he had to live away from his tribe, serving a leader to whom he was not related by blood.

The emir grew to depend on Munthir. First Munthir was made chief of the light raiders, then leader of the heavy raiders who fought as they raided. Then Munthir was made leader of the main army itself. The emir said, "I have rewarded your strength and bravery. But I hope to reward your wisdom. Someday you will be a chief of my government."

"Soon I will move on," Munthir said. "I am without a tribe. There is no place for me."

"You need roots," the emir said. "You are like a weed blown about by desert winds. There is only one way you can get roots. You must start your family."

"There is no woman for me," Munthir said.

"There is my daughter," said the emir. "Marry her. Make this your home. Make my family your family. And one day you will rule Uman in my place."

"Perhaps you are right," Munthir said.

Munthir was married. At first he was happy, for the princess was even more beautiful than Hasna. But years passed and no children came. Munthir talked to the wisest men, but none could give him an answer.

"I, of all men, must have children," Munthir said. "Without children I am without roots. Without roots I am as nothing."

One night as he was standing a night watch alone, Munthir looked at his hundred men sleeping near the dying fire. "Perhaps I am as nothing," he said, "but a hundred men depend on me. Back in Uman there are thousands who depend on me."

So Munthir decided that he would drift no more like a weed blown by desert winds. He would think no longer about having children. It was a sorrow he must endure. Better not to think about it.

To stop thinking of his sorrow, Munthir thought of home and the Bani Hilal. He thought of his boyhood when his father had given him everything possible. I wronged my father, Munthir thought. I wished for impossible things. When they could not be given, I blamed my father. Then he said aloud, "Bless Abu Hilal wherever he may be."

For many years Abu Hilal had grieved over the loss of his favorite son. But he never spoke aloud of it. He would not even let himself think the name *Munthir*. Munthir was dead for Abu Hilal. He never expected to hear of his son again. His son must have been killed by the wild desert tribes.

One day as Abu Hilal, now an old, old man, looked out of his tent at his flocks and herds and many children and kinsmen, he could not keep the name Munthir from his mind. Abu Hilal cried aloud, "Munthir, Munthir, my son. All of this should belong to you. Where is my beloved son?"

From that day on no name was as sweet to the ears of Abu Hilal as the name of Munthir. A singing girl came to the tent of Abu Hilal and chanted the name over and over in her sweet voice. To such a chant Abu Hilal went to sleep, and to such a chant he woke in the morning. One morning Abu Hilal woke to the chant and cried aloud, "May Munthir be blessed. May he be blessed wherever he is."

And from that day Munthir was indeed blessed. His wife conceived and brought forth a strong son. As soon as the first child was born, Munthir called all of the people of Uman to attend a great feast. "I am blessed," Munthir told them. "I have a son. But as long as I stay here, my father is without his son. I must go to the land of Bani Hilal, and give my father back his son."

"No!" the people shouted. "You are our king. You belong here."

"Here I will return," Munthir said. "But first I must let my father know that I am alive. As I have been given a son, so must I give him a son. Then I will return."

Munthir traveled to the land of Hilal, and again Abu Hilal had a son, his favorite son. And Munthir discovered that his good fortune had begun on the day he had blessed his father, and his father had blessed him in return.

3

A BATTLE AND A WEDDING

And there lived a *shereff* (nobleman) of Mecca who was of the Bani Hilal. A king of the Roum marched against Mecca, and the *shereff* called on his tribe for help. From Nejd and Yeman, from Hijaz and Tahamah, the tribesmen of Bani Hilal rode in to fight the soldiers of the Roum who formed in three great columns on the Plain of Tai'f.

The Hilalies held the hills. Behind every rock and stone a Hilali warrior waited for the signal to rush down on the men of Roum.

Now the King of Roum saw that his spies had told him wrong. Instead of facing a few tribesmen of Mecca, he faced Arabs from five kingdoms. To his vizier he said, "These Hilalies are united. They flow together as many drops of water that form a stream. Now the stream becomes a river. Soon the river will be a sea. How can we stand against so many?"

"There is no need," the vizier said. "These Arabs would rather see one great hero fight another in single combat than win a kingdom. Let one of our champions fight one of theirs. Let the war depend on the single battle."

"Be it so," the King of Roum agreed. "Against their hero we will send the Blood Drinker. Then there will be no question how the battle will turn out."

The challenge was sent to the Hilalies in the hills. From the hills a great cheer came, for the Hilalies loved sport and single combat. So many Hilalies wished to fight the hero of Roum that the *shereff* could not choose one without starting a war among his own men. Lots were drawn and Malik of Yemen won. He fastened on his coat of Persian chain mail, hefted his Indian sword and Hindustan shield and walked down toward the plain.

In the ranks of the Roum the drums began to beat. A great iron cage was rolled to the front. In the iron cage, so awful that Roum soldiers looked away as the cage passed, was the Blood Drinker. Spearmen with long poles pushed the cage. Bowmen kept their arrows pointed toward the cage. For the Blood Drinker was more beast than man, and the soldiers of Roum did not know which way he would turn when the cage was opened.

When the drums stopped, the doors would open. The Blood Drinker would be pushed forward. And he would face the unlucky hero of the Hilalies. Oh, this Blood Drinker! He had been found as a wild boy on the northern steppes. His spirit was that of a wolf. His body was that of a bear. Yet because he had been born of woman, his cunning was that of a man.

Malik, slowed by his heavy armor, came down from the hill. The cage was pushed to the front. The drums continued to boom. Malik could not see inside the cage, for he had closed the visor of his Aadite helmet. He turned and waved to his brothers in the hills.

Watching him, the King of Roum said, "Be happy now. Soon the Blood Drinker will be on you." To the spearmen near the cage, the king called, "Stand ready to stop the drums. Stand ready to lift the gate. Bring forward the Blood Drinker's falchion (curved sword) and cup. And see that he does not turn on us."

The spearmen and bowmen made a ring behind the cage. Torches were fired and stuck in the sand so that the man-beast could not turn back without running through a wall of fire. The Blood Drinker had been trained to fear only fire. "Stop the drums," the king commanded.

There was silence. Malik, looking toward the enemy, saw only the cage with the wall of fire behind it. "I came to fight a man, not to slay an animal," he cried. "Where is your hero? Out with him!"

"Lift the bars," the king ordered. "Drive him forward."

But there was no need to urge the beast forward. The Blood Drinker came roaring out of the cage. In one bound he was on

Malik's chest. With one sweep his falchion cut through Malik. At the sight of blood he called a wild and fierce cry, and Malik was lost beneath his hairy bulk. He whirled about to charge the soldiers of Roum, but the fire stopped him. He turned toward the hills.

Finished with Malik, the Blood Drinker charged forward swinging his bloody falchion. The Hilalies fell back before this terrible sight. Brave warriors who feared no man alive tumbled over each other to get away from the Blood Drinker. The *shereff* himself was nearly trampled, and would have been except for one Hilali, Rizk by name.

"Do you run from a mere animal?" Rizk called. "Learn from our enemies. Fight fire with fire."

Rizk seized torches that had been readied for the night camp. Striking a flint, he lit four of the torches. Then he ran down the slope toward the charging man-beast.

One torch Rizk threw in front of the Blood Drinker, and his charge was stopped. One, Rizk threw to the right of the creature. When he charged to the left, there Rizk threw the third torch. The fourth torch he thrust toward the Blood Drinker. When the awful fighter of the Roum struck at the torch, Rizk cut the falchion from his hairy hand. Then Rizk drove him down into the ranks of the Roum, and the enemy were scattered across the plain. While the Roum warriors were slaying the Blood Drinker, the Hilalies charged and routed them.

After the battle, the *shereff* sent for Rizk. Rizk entered the great silk tent of the *shereff* of Mecca. Rizk was seated on the

thickest, finest carpets; his head was pillowed on the softest cushions. Music was played and candied dates were served.

"My home is your home," the *shereff* told him. "Before you now will come the fairest women of Arabia — my three daughters. Choose one. Whichever of the three you choose will be your bride."

A cymbal sounded and a beautiful woman entered the tent and knelt on the red carpets. "I choose her," Rizk said. "She will be my bride. What is her name?"

"Her name is Selma. But wait. You have not seen the others."

"I am happy with this one," said Rizk. "I need see no more."

"You have chosen well," the *shereff* said. "I had the fairest come first to punish the man who is never pleased, and who always must wait to see the others. Had you not chosen her first, she would never have been truly yours."

The wedding feast was held on the plain near Mecca while all the tribes of Bani Hilal were still gathered. In the center of the plain a great circle was carpeted with marigolds and primroses. Around the field of flowers the land was cleared for war games. Thousands of war horses pawed and stamped. Armed riders dueled with wooden swords and jousted with blunted spears. No one could see the sky because of a black canopy of arrows shot up by the archers and bowmen. Falcons wheeled aloft to guide hunters. Powerful wrestlers grunted and heaved and dashed each other onto the hard ground.

Inside the ring of flowers everything was different. Selma's tent was made of red silk, so rich and pure that robes and gowns for the finest women of the tribes could have been made from it. Inside the tent were walls of golden thread. Selma's chair was of ivory, and the legs rested on four knobs of gold, polished so that they could be seen two days' journey away. In front of Selma's chair, women musicians touched their strings and beat drums, and lovely girls danced the *dubkeh* on the thick carpet of flowers. And they danced to the even beat of the *durbukeh* across the flowery fields.

When the chief justice Budair signed the marriage certificate, ten thousand maids of the tribe struck a high beautiful note and held it for many minutes. The marriage of Rizk and Selma was done. An old crone cut the sand and told the fortune of the couple.

"From this match will come the greatest son of Bani Hilal," she said. "But his coming will at first bring no joy."

"Bah!" Rizk shouted at the old woman. "Give me a man son, and all will be happy."

For many days the feasts and contests went on. So generous was the *shereff* of Mecca that he would not let the feasting end until one hundred camels had been killed and eaten. But the day did come when the tribes had to set out for their distant lands.

Before Rizk returned to the land where he was prince, the father of Selma called him aside. "There is one thing you must know," he said. "In ancient times some of my family fought for the princes of Abyssinia, and married Abyssinian princesses. Though our blood is that of their kings, in each generation a few dark sons are born. If this happens, be not surprised, and think no evil of my daughter."

"Have no fear," Rizk said. "No child of Selma's could be less bright than the sun to me."

4

ABU ZAID THE HILALI

Selma journeyed to the land of Rizk, her prince. In the first
year she gave birth to a beautiful little girl. They called her
Sheeha. She was the fairest child in Hijaz. Years then passed,
but no other child was born. It seemed that no son would be
born to inherit the vast lands and wealth of Rizk. This troubled Rizk greatly and to forget, he went often to war. The more
he fought with neighboring kings and tribes, the more land he
conquered. The more land he conquered, the more he was troubled because he had no son to inherit it. So it went. Rizk grew
fiercer and his lands increased, but no son came.

Selma was also troubled. She was often left alone while Rizk
made new wars, and she worried and did not sleep. To forget
her troubles she worked like a serving girl, even carrying her

own water from the well. One day as she sat beside the well waiting to fill her jug with water, a blackbird flew by. Troubled, unhappy and alone, Selma called out, "I wish to God that I could give my prince a boy — be he as black as that bird."

Selma's wish was heard and granted. She did give birth to a boy. And the boy was far darker than she or her husband. The boy's birth was under favorable signs. As the news was brought to Rizk, he also learned that five hundred she-camels were born to his people on that same day. And on that same day, five hundred horses were born, all well marked and healthy. Rizk was overjoyed with his great good news. He rushed to see his man child. He cared nothing about his color. A son had been born to inherit his land.

The day came when relatives and kinsmen were to present their *nukut* (gifts to honor a newborn son). On that day when kinsmen came with gifts, Rizk and Selma had to display their child to their relatives.

All noticed the color of the child, but thinking that perhaps the servants had exposed him to the sun and used too much oil on his skin, they said nothing. They pretended great joy. And they marveled at his size. For truly the son was huge, with the shoulders and arms of the mighty Rizk.

All were silent about the color, except an emir named Serhan. Seeing the baby, Serhan was amazed and spoke out, "He seems dark. Far darker than any child of this tribe that I have ever seen."

Rizk for the first time noticed the color of his son, and turning to his wife, said, "Serhan speaks the truth. Why is our child darker than others?"

Selma, confused, began, "I wished it so — "

"You wished it so! Say no more! I divorce you," said Rizk. He said the words three times and then nothing could be done. Selma left her husband and daughter, and with her new son started back to the tents of her father, the *shereff* of Mecca. As she left, she cursed Serhan, saying, "May God cause unhappiness to him who caused me and my child this grief."

Selma did not return to the tents of her father. She feared to tell her father about her child, Barakat, who was darker than other children of the tribe. Selma blamed herself for her foolish wish. Instead of going home, Selma went to live with the tribe of the Sheikh Zahlan, an old friend of her father's. She asked Zahlan not to tell her father.

Zahlan took Selma and Barakat into his tribe. He loved the boy, Barakat, and raised him as his own son. Barakat grew to great size, and, when only a boy, was riding in the *gom* of Zahlan. He thought of Zahlan as his father; he called him "Father," and he was known as the "dark son of Zahlan." Zahlan soon saw that of all his many sons, Barakat alone would be a warrior who could protect the rich meadow lands of the Bani Zahlan. Zahlan, who was old and feeble, rejoiced in his adopted son.

A day came when the lands of Rizk suffered from a long drought. Where there had been grain and flowers, only thorn and cactus grew. Sand dunes, like white monsters, crept closer to the tents of Rizk, and camels and horses had to be driven great distances for water. The tribe began to move to the west, until it crossed the Jabal Shaytan and looked down on the meadows of Zahlan. "On that rich land we must settle," Rizk said.

"What of the Bani Zahlan?" his counselors asked him.

"They can have our old land. We must drive them into the desert. They are rabbits."

That night the *gom* of Rizk raided into the lands of Zahlan. But they found no rabbits. The *gom* met a raiding party led by Barakat, son of Zahlan. The men of Rizk were driven off, and as they rode away Barakat raised his javelin and threw it with great force. The javelin passed through the backs and out the fronts of three riders of Rizk's *gom*. When the soldiers saw three men of the *gom* fastened together with one long javelin, they were surprised and frightened.

"*Ya Allah,*" they said, "they are not rabbits in that valley. Perhaps we should ride around them."

"Never," said Rizk. "Bani Hilal never are beaten by such people. This is no work of the tribe of Zahlan. Of all men, only a man of Hilal could throw a javelin with such force. But that is impossible. Therefore it must be a jinni who protects them in the night. Tomorrow we will attack in the day. Send our greatest young heroes forth with the challenge."

In the morning the heroes of Rizk challenged the heroes of Zahlan. In truth there was only one hero of Zahlan — Barakat.

But to fool the enemy, Zahlan sent Barakat out each time in different clothes.

One after another of the warriors of Rizk was defeated by the hero of Zahlan. The men of Rizk did not know that each time it was the same man in different dress. "Bah," Rizk said, "this proves nothing. I will challenge Zahlan himself."

So Rizk and Zahlan fought, and Zahlan was cut from his horse by the sweep of Rizk's scimiter. Rizk would have finished Zahlan, but Barakat drove him off.

From in front of his army, Rizk called, "I have beaten your king. Be wise and surrender."

From the ranks of Zahlan came an answering call, "You have cut down the old tree. But a strong young shoot lives. You must kill the king's son, Barakat, before we will give in to you."

"Agreed," Rizk shouted and spurred his horse forward to meet Barakat. I must finish him quickly, Rizk thought, because night comes on and their protecting jinni will come. *Ya hai!* Look at this one who rides so swiftly against me. He is like a piece of the night himself. But I'll soon unhorse him.

Instead, Barakat's horse jumped right over Rizk, and Barakat struck Rizk to the ground. But Rizk was too cunning to be taken easily. He had fought in many battles. Barakat had fought in few. What Rizk lacked in strength and speed he made up in experience. Each time that Barakat slashed at Rizk, the older man avoided him. Still, Rizk, his eyes blinded by sweat and his heart exploding with fatigue and age, knew that he could never win against the young warrior. "Let us hold for a moment," Rizk cried. "Let us stop. Come to my lines for a cooling drink. Once refreshed we will fight some more."

"Granted," Barakat said, and thought to himself, it matters not how long it takes, old man. You are finished. It will do no harm to give you one last cool drink to wet your tongue for your supper with Death.

Back in Rizk's camp, cooled drinks were brought. Now I must strike, Rizk thought, as Barakat raised the goblet to drink. So Rizk began to slide his sword from its scabbard. But from her *howdaj* (riding platform on a camel) Sheeha, Rizk's daughter, saw her father's evil move. She did not recognize Barakat as her brother, but she called out,

"Take care, Barakat. He means to kill you by surprise."

Barakat at once drew his sword. The drinking goblets were kicked aside, and the fight went on, more furiously than before. Again Barakat attacked and Rizk defended, and the men rolled into the long, purple shadows that were moving out onto the plain. The jinni will surely come soon, Rizk thought. We must end this for tonight.

"Young warrior," he called, "soon it will be night. It would not be fair if this fight went on. I am old and my eyes are dimmed. Let us begin the fight again tomorrow, for already I cannot see you. I claim this right by my age."

"By my sword (I grant you mercy)," Barakat said. "It would be better to put your head on a pole in daylight. Then it can be seen from greater distance, and other scoundrels will avoid the lands of Zahlan. Go, old man. You are beaten anyway."

So tired was Rizk that he could not walk back to his tent without the help of two young men. In his tent Rizk raged like a lion.

"Bring my daughter Sheeha to me," he shouted. "I will burn her for betraying her father."

When Sheeha came before her father, she said, "I did not betray you. I saved you by saving your honor. Your name would have been lost forever if you killed that warrior by trickery. You would never rule here or anywhere."

When Rizk heard his daughter, he knew that she spoke the truth. "If that was the only reason then I pardon you," he said. "I was too anxious to kill him. I did not think."

"That was not the only reason," Sheeha said, "though I thank you for the pardon. I learned the name of that warrior. It is Barakat, the same name my brother had. Because of him you divorced my mother. And that was a bad thing. Did you not note how dark was Barakat, son of Zahlan? His other two sons are light. Why didn't Zahlan divorce his wife when she brought forth one darker than the others? Zahlan is greater than you. As a result he now has a great hero son, while you, old and tired, must fight our battles. We will lose because of your great pride."

Hearing this, some of the nobles of Rizk wished to learn more of Barakat, son of Zahlan. From a tribesman of the *shereff*, they learned that Selma had never gone back to the tent of her father. From a prisoner of the army of Zahlan, they learned that the name of Barakat's mother was Selma and that he was not the true son of Zahlan.

In the morning, nobles rode out to the field with Rizk. When Barakat approached they said, "You cannot go on with this unequal fight. This man, Rizk, our leader, is your true father. How can you slay him for Zahlan?"

Rizk, deeply ashamed, said nothing. Although he could not lift his sword arm, he would not beg for his life.

Barakat sat silently on his horse and watched his father. How shall I choose, he wondered? Here before me, this tired old man, is my natural father. When I was a baby he would not have me because I was a little darker than other children. He even sent my mother away. Now he comes to take the land of Zahlan, the only man I have ever loved. Yet Rizk is my real father. How can I forget that?

"What do you say, noble Rizk?" Barakat asked. "Is your life sweet?"

"I say nothing," Rizk answered. "My life has never been as sweet to me as my honor. Do what you will. I am ready to fight, and if necessary to die. There is a time for everything."

He is a proud man, thought Barakat. And it was this very pride that made him send my mother away years ago.

"Let Rizk defend himself," Barakat said. "He chose not to be my father. Zahlan chose to be my father. For Zahlan I will fight. He gave refuge to my mother. He fed me, loved me, taught me, and trained me. He is the father I love. And this

man Rizk has injured him. Let him ride forward. I will knock
him from his horse and lead him to Zahlan's bedside. I will let
Zahlan decide what will become of Rizk. Let him fight or I will
charge and kill all of you."

The nobles rode quickly back to their lines, and Rizk was
left alone facing his son and enemy. Rizk now knew there was
no jinni in the land of Zahlan. It was Barakat who threw the
javelin that pierced three men.

"I will never be made a slave," Rizk snarled as he prepared
to charge. "I die or conquer."

Barakat charged. Rizk tried to lift his sword but could not. With his last strength, Rizk ducked Barakat's sword, but the wind of its passing tumbled Rizk to the ground and he was knocked senseless by the fall. Barakat tied a cord around his neck and led him to the bedside of Zahlan.

Before Zahlan, Barakat said, "Father, what will you have me to do with this man who caused you injury?"

At that moment Selma came into the chambers weeping. "Let him go, if you love me," she said. "He is your true father. You would live cursed if you harmed him."

All eyes turned toward the dying Sheikh Zahlan, who alone had the right to decide. With his failing strength Zahlan said, "Spare him. By honoring him you will honor me. But you can honor me more before I die. Since I am not your true father you may take as wife one of my daughters. Which do you choose?"

"Ghosn el Ban is my choice," said Barakat. "I have loved her since I was a child. As I thought of her as my sister, I never hoped to marry her."

So the marriage was arranged, and Zahlan died happy.

"Would you return to me?" Rizk asked Selma. "I was wrong. I have never taken another wife since you left."

"It is my father who must decide," Selma told him.

The *shereff* decreed that his daughter should return to Rizk. "Since I never knew that she left, it is as though it never happened."

Selma and Rizk settled in the lands of Barakat and lived happily as they had in the first years of their marriage.

From the day of his marriage, Barakat was called Abu Zaid the Hilali. He was to be the greatest warrior of the Hilalies. From that day on, the Bani Hilal would be stronger than all other tribes, for no warrior could stand against Abu Zaid.

5

THE PRICE OF A CURSE

It was Serhan who first spoke of the color of the child who was to become Abu Zaid. Because his words caused Selma to be driven from the tents of Rizk, she cursed this man who caused her unhappiness. And the curse of Selma clung to Serhan, son of the Emir Zohair.

Serhan grew in strength and wisdom until he was the greatest of the sons of Zohair. He was respected by all men and admired by all women. And a day came when the tribe had its tents on the hills near the meadows of Dula, and Emir Zohair lay dying.

"Bring my son Serhan to me," Zohair commanded, "for he is the wisest of all Hilal. He will become emir in my place."

But then, lying back to rest, Zohair was sad, for he remembered that Serhan had neither wife nor child. When Serhan came to the tent of his father, he knew that the bird of death beat its dark wings just above the ridge pole. Yet the old emir had strength to give one last order.

"You must marry," Zohair commanded his son. "You must marry no mean slave woman, but a princess. You will be emir of the Hilal. She must be fit to be your queen. In some land a princess waits for you. Go! Find her!"

"I promise, Father," said Serhan.

Hearing this promise, Zohair closed his eyes and died.

Serhan prepared to search for a princess. To the tents of Hilal came poets and singers who had traveled through Arabia and all other lands. These poets had sung in all courts and looked on all beauty. Serhan ordered them to describe in poetry the most beautiful princess they had seen.

Thobyan described a princess of the Suleym whose eyes were like campfires, beckoning to a hunter lost in the desert. Serhan shook his head. "I want no such fire in my tent," he said. "That one would cause trouble."

Malec described a princess of the Fire Worshipers who moved like a cloud across parched sand, full to bursting with rain. "She is dark and calm and above the world," said Malec.

Serhan shook his head. "She is not for me. I wish to spend my days down on earth with my kinsmen and friends. She is too high and mighty."

Then Yashcor spoke: "The sun burns above, so that sky and earth melt together and there is no horizon. You and your horse face this terrible glare. On the whole waste of bare sand there is only one lovely, thin-stemmed reed that sways with a new breeze. You go on. The reed bends above a rivulet of sweet water. You go on. In the rushes near this heaven-sent rivulet is a lovely gazelle, dark of eye and soft. That is Shamma, Princess of Josham. Will you go on?"

"Say no more," said Serhan, "I will have her."

"The journey to her country is forty days."

"If it be four hundred," said Serhan, "I will have her. We leave at once."

A great party of Hilali horsemen set out for the land of Josham. Serhan rode at their head. Messengers brought alarm to the King of Josham and his ministers. "A *gom* of the Bani Hilal approaches our northern borders."

"Prepare to fight," the king ordered.

But when the Hilali horsemen drew near, the king could see that they came in peace. The king ordered thirty camels slaughtered, and the men of Josham and the men of Hilal feasted. The feast went on for three days. On the fourth day it was fitting to ask the Hilalies why they had come to the lands of Josham.

Serhan's oldest adviser spoke, "We want one of the daughters of the king for our prince — the Emir of Hilal.

"I see," said the King of Josham. "One of my daughters. I have many."

Serhan wished to shout out the name of Shamma, but this could not be done. Only the king could choose the daughter. What happened, happened.

"Very well," the king's advisers agreed. "The king will decide."

That night the king went to his first wife to ask about his daughters. "The Hilalies are great. One of my daughters must stand well for us. Which will it be? Wallada?"

"No," said the king's wife. "She is not grand, nor can she be. One day she thrust her hand into the cooking pot to taste the food."

"She is not grand," the king agreed. "What of Leila?"

His wife shook her head. "Once when I was ill, Leila was given to a lowly woman to nurse. And from that low woman Leila took her temper. She will not do."

"What of our daughter Shamma?" the king asked.

"Shamma is perfect," her mother said. "But because I am her own mother, I wish one thing for her. She is the most modest and pure of all of our girls. The wedding will be celebrated in the land of Hilal. That is a long journey. Ask the prince of Hilal not to look at her until after he has reached his land and the wedding is over."

"I will tell him so," the king promised.

So the marriage to Serhan the cursed was arranged. But when the king told him of the condition, Serhan was worried. Why should such a condition be made? he wondered. Perhaps she is ugly. Perhaps the poet lied and this king tricks me.

Seeing that Serhan hesitated, the king agreed to a huge dowry if the condition would be met. Shamma's mother added a necklace that was worth an entire kingdom. So Serhan agreed to the condition, though his heart was troubled.

How the men and women of the tribe will laugh at me if she is ugly, Serhan thought. How terrible it will be if, when we reach our land, I have brought with me not the most beautiful woman but the most ugly.

Each night, during the long journey homeward, Serhan stared into the campfire and worried. His pride was great and he did not want the men and women of Bani Hilal to laugh at him. One night, he could stand the worry no longer. He left the dying fire and crept to the closed tent of Shamma. If she is ugly, he promised himself, I will send her back to her father's tents. Or perhaps I will even kill her for tricking me.

Serhan softly pulled back the flap of the tent and peered inside. Shamma lay fast asleep. She had loosened her long hair and it hung down and covered her beautiful white face. When he saw her like this in the dim light, Serhan — who knew little of women — gave an angry growl. She is like an animal! A woman like that for an emir! No wonder her father made such a condition.

Serhan ran to his tent to get his sword. I'll kill her here and now and be done with this trick, he raged. She looks more like an animal than a human.

Serhan came back, swinging his long Indian sword over his head. He sliced away the whole side of the tent and burst in on Shamma. Shamma started up in her bed. The hair fell away from her beautiful face and neck. The moonlight clearly showed

Serhan that his promised bride was more beautiful than any woman he had ever seen. He stood for a moment in stunned silence, but Shamma, seeing the sword in his hand, screamed and tore at the sparkling necklace around her neck.

The string snapped and the necklace fell to the ground. At that very moment a great, dark bird flew through the torn side of the tent and seized the necklace in its talons. Then with a dreadful cry and a beating of its powerful wings, it was gone into the night.

With a sob of sorrow, Serhan ran after the night bird. He knew that he had wronged his bride-to-be and he was determined to get back her jewels. Seeing the bird framed against the moonlight, Serhan raced through the night, across the sand, up over rocky hills and down to a smooth, white beach near the sea.

But the bird flew out over the dark waves, the necklace still dangling from its claws. Serhan paced up and down the sand. It is my fault, he thought bitterly. My curse is to be passed on, even to my beautiful princess. Because of me she has lost her priceless necklace. Serhan walked and cried and wailed; but the bird did not return, and finally Serhan fell down and slept on the sand.

While Serhan lay senseless on the beach, a dark, slender ship landed silently beside him, and the crew fell on Serhan and took his sword. Though he was unarmed, Serhan fought until his face was covered with blood. And even as the men dragged him toward the boat, Serhan — using his own blood — wrote a message on a rock.

The next day Shamma stayed in her tent. She lay under her silken covers and her heart beat fast as she wondered about Serhan and about why he had not returned. On the second night one of Shamma's own servants came to the tent.

"Rise and flee," the servant warned her. "Your brave husband-to-be chased the night bird to the sea, but there he was captured by strange men from another land. Now these wild Hilali warriors are quarreling over which one will take you."

"How can a woman alone escape?" Shamma asked.

"I have taken clothes from Serhan's tent," said her servant. "You must put them on and run away. You must keep the disguise of a man."

"I will run away," said Shamma, "but somewhere I will find the man to whom I was promised. He alone will be my husband. When I saw him in the moonlight I knew he was a great warrior and the only man for me. I am sure that he came to my tent to guard me from harm in the night."

Shamma fled from the tents of the Hilalies. She ran back to where Serhan had crossed the hills to the sea. She ran along the same beach crying out and seeking him. Finally she tired and fell asleep on the sand, just as he had done. In the morning she found the rock where Serhan had written his message in his own blood. She sat for many days in this spot, eating sparingly of the small bit of food that she had.

And one day a boat landed and men, the same ones who had captured Serhan, took Shamma as a slave. "He is a thin, delicate boy," the slave raiders said, "but he is beautiful. Perhaps the king will want him to serve inside the palace. He seems to be of royal appearance."

Shamma said nothing during the whole voyage to the distant land. She decided to stay as a boy until she found Serhan.

At the palace of the king, Shamma said that her name was Shamman. The king was pleased with Shamma's appearance, and he sent her to serve in the chambers of the princess. Each morning Shamma brought fruit to the bedside of the princess.

For the first few mornings a soldier watched from behind a curtain. Seeing that Shamma was always gentle and kind to the princess, the soldier reported this to the king.

"He is a fine boy," the king said. "We need watch him no longer. I will make him the guardian and servant of my daughter."

Though things went well with Shamma at the palace, Serhan suffered. For many days he was kept in chains. When he was released, he tried to seize a sword and escape, because he was a warrior of Hilal. But he was taken again. Since he could not be trusted near the palace he was sent far from the city to a lonely valley. There he was forced to tend swine. He was left alone, and he lived with no company but the swine and the birds and beasts of the forest. He thought only of Shamma, and how he had injured her. He planned day and night to find the necklace and return it.

In the palace the king's daughter fell in love with Shamman. To test his worth the king made Shamma a tax collector in one of the most troublesome provinces. But Shamma had no trouble. She won the friendship of the fiercest men of the province and the king's tax payments were greater than they ever had been. Shamma was brought back to the capital city. Preparations were made for the wedding.

As the day of the wedding came near, Shamma avoided seeing the princess. Actually Shamma loved the princess better than a sister and did not want to make her sad. Shamma tried to go back to the distant province, but the king would not permit it. What shall I do, Shamma wondered? If I tell them that I am a woman I will be given as a wife to one of these nobles. I will never see Serhan again. Shamma decided to confess her secret to the princess, and she went to her sleeping room in the night.

The princess was very frightened. "Shamman, why have you come here?" she whispered. "If they find you here now, you will be killed."

"Be not afraid," Shamma said. "Have I not always been gentle and kind to you?"

"Yes," said the princess. "For that reason I love you. You are the most gentle and kind person I have ever known. But if the guards find you here, we can never be married."

"We can never be married," Shamma said. "I am gentle because I am like you — a woman. I came seeking my husband-to-be, and I was captured by your people. Since I wore the clothes of a man, I was taken as a man."

Shamma then told the princess her strange story. Afterwards the princess cried and stroked Shamma's hand. "Never mind," the princess said. "I have found a loving sister in you. Together we will find your husband Serhan. He must be in this kingdom somewhere. Perhaps in a distant place." The princess promised to help Shamma find Serhan, and she promised to keep her secret.

Serhan was truly in a distant place, still tending swine in his lonely valley. He knew now that he could escape any time he wished. He had only to walk away. But he could not go without the necklace of Shamma. He knew that it was somewhere in the land, because the night bird had flown in this direction across the dark sea. Serhan spent each day searching the forests and meadows. He was still a prisoner until he could find the necklace.

One day, tired after a long search, Serhan lay down in the shade of a tamarisk tree. He slept and as always his dreams were of Shamma and the beauty of the face he had seen but once in the moonlight.

A bird began to peck at Serhan's cheek. Angrily, he brushed the bird aside. The bird hopped away and then came back. Serhan struck at the bird but still it came back. Finally Serhan sat up. The bird flew into the tamarisk tree.

This bird seems to lead me to this tree, Serhan thought. How strange! Most birds keep men away from their nests. Serhan finally rose and climbed the tree. And there he found it — the beautiful necklace of Shamma glittering in the sunlight that filtered through the tamarisk leaves. Serhan lifted out the necklace and the bird showed signs of great happiness.

Serhan was now free to leave the forests. He started the long journey back toward the sea. He traveled by day, and out of haste he traveled also by night. One night a band of robbers leaped from a roadside wood and knocked Serhan down. They took his clothes and the necklace and left him bleeding in the dust.

In the city, the robbers sold the necklace to a merchant. The merchant knew that only the king could afford such jewels, so he took the necklace to the palace. The king had just died and Shamma served the princess as adviser. The merchant came before the princess and Shamma to show the necklace.

"Merchant," cried Shamma, "where did you get this beautiful necklace? It is fit for a princess."

"That is true," the merchant said happily. "And to a princess it belonged. In the Land of the Tigris, I saved a princess from robbers. This necklace was given to me as a reward. I would never sell it, except that one of my caravans has been plundered. I must have money."

"You lie," Shamma said. "This is my necklace, stolen from me by a bird of night. A man went in search of it. Perhaps he found it. Now where did you get it? Did you kill him? Tell me! Speak!"

The merchant, a very frightened man, told the truth. The chief of the robbers was brought before Shamma. The chief, a tall, strong man, would say nothing. The royal torturers took him away, and before he had gone five steps with them he spoke the truth. He described the man they had robbed, and Shamma knew that she had found her husband at last.

Horsemen with a covered litter were sent out along the road to find Serhan. He was brought back to the palace, and his wounds were so serious that he did not recognize Shamma. Each night she sat at his bedside cooling his forehead with water, and rubbing his hands and wrists with oil and balm. But he said nothing to her.

Staring down at Serhan, Shamma was sad. I have been foolish, she thought. Why should he know or love me, after all this time? He has suffered and he has forgotten. Each day his body grows stronger, but his love for me grows no stronger.

One night Shamma decided to test Serhan. She had the princess dressed in her finest robes. Serhan was propped up in his bed and the princess entered the room. She wore Shamma's necklace. Shamma watched everything from behind a curtain. Serhan started in surprise when he saw the necklace.

"Where did you get those jewels?" he asked.

"They are mine," the princess said. "They were given to me because I am the fairest woman in the world."

Serhan was silent. He was planning how to get the necklace from the princess and escape. But Shamma, watching him, could not know his thoughts. He is agreeing, she thought. He agrees with her silently. He thinks she is the fairest.

"Do you not agree that I am the fairest in the world?" the princess asked. "And I am the richest woman of the world. This is my kingdom. My father is dead. I need a man to take the throne. I have picked you. You need only say that I am the fairest woman of the world. Why are you silent? Speak! Remember you are in my palace. I saved you."

"I am grateful to you for saving me," said Serhan. "In my sick dreams I remembered that a handsome youth sat at my bedside."

"My cousin," said the princess. "Now speak. Say the words. This kingdom is yours. I can be your queen."

"I cannot say the words," Serhan said. He leaped from his

bed, and snatched the necklace. "And this does not belong to you. It belongs to my beloved, who really is the fairest. And if it costs me my head I will return it to her."

He stuffed the necklace in his belt and began to run. But the guards seized him and dragged him back before the princess and Shamma.

Shamma looked at Serhan. "Poor fool," Shamma said. "You must love this woman a great deal to lose your life for her. What is the name of such a fair one?"

"Shamma," said Serhan.

"I am she," said Shamma happily. "I am the one you seek."

With these words, Shamma removed the turban that hid her beautiful hair, and it fell in dark curls around her shoulders. The amazed Serhan could not speak, but the light of joy in his eyes made words unnecessary.

With blessings and gifts of the princess, Shamma and Serhan returned to the land of Hilal. There Shamma was queen and Serhan was emir. A son was born to them, and the son was named Hassan, which means good. Hassan was to be the greatest emir of the Bani Hilal.

Great then was the fortune of the Bani Hilal. They had a great warrior, Abu Zaid. And when Hassan grew to manhood they were to have a great emir. The curse on Serhan in the end had brought a blessing to the tents of the Hilal because he had proved himself a brave and true man.

6

RESCUE FROM THE FIRE WORSHIPERS

Along tall dunes, on the western borders of Hilal, sped a
messenger on a camel which moved like a wind in the high
heavens, so swiftly that the sand was not disturbed by its passing. The Hilal lookouts, recognizing him as a friendly rider,
waved their spears and gave him safe passage. The rider sped
his camel to the very tent of Emir Serhan and stopped in towering dust, as the camel's feet seemed to touch the earth at last.

The camel dipped. The rider slid down and spoke to the Hilali
spearman who stood guard at the station: "From Queen
Kherma of the Yemen I bring greetings to Serhan, mighty Emir
of Hilal. The tales of the great goodness and bravery of Emir
Serhan's son Hassan are sung throughout the Yemen. May I
enter?"

Fires were kindled and food was prepared. The messenger feasted on lamb and fruit and tender camel flesh. He praised Serhan and Hassan and told of his own queen, Kherma of the Yemen. Talk continued into the night, and when the time was right, the messenger complimented the food and the hospitality of the Hilal.

"You are as great as I have heard," he said. "No tribe is more generous than the Bani Hilal."

"The time has come for speaking what is in your heart," said Emir Serhan. "Without a Hilali friend to guarantee your safety you have ridden through our lands. Truly your camel has flown here. Speak that we may know the reason."

Thus commanded, the messenger, a prince of Yemen, spoke: "Suleiman, young prince of Yemen and brother of Kherma, has been captured by the Fire Worshipers (Persians). They have taken him to their wild lands to the north. The loss of this youth of beauty is mourned by all our people, and by the queen, his sister. But she has hope. She has heard of the bravery of your son Hassan. She knows that he alone could rescue her brother from the Fire Worshipers."

Emir Serhan stroked a beard that had gone gray from trouble. He had but one son. Hassan, though already a leader of men of the *gom,* was young. The lands of the Fire Worshipers were distant. The people there wore the strongest armor and swung the keenest swords of the world. The fire they worshiped gave strength to their blades.

"I will think of it," Serhan promised.

The messenger nodded and departed, but later, he went to the tent of Hassan with the Queen Kherma's plea for help. Hassan said, "I will go. I will free the lady's brother, whatever the hardship. My men will be ready to ride before tomorrow's sun appears."

Hassan roused his men and they began to work through the night, preparing the horses and camels for the journey. The sound of women filling jugs at the well woke Queen Shamma. She went to the door of the tent and saw that the women were the wives of Hassan's raiders. She woke Emir Serhan.

"What is this?" she asked. "Where are the raiders of our son going that they must prepare for a journey in the dark of night? What rash thought moves our son?"

Serhan rose raging. He knew that the man from Yemen had sent a message to Hassan. In his long robes, taller in the moonlight than any of the Bani Hilal, Serhan strode into the center of the camping place.

"Stop your work," he commanded Hassan's men. "What moon madness is this? Where are you going?"

"We follow our master to the land of the Fire Worshipers," the men said.

"I ask you to refuse my son's command," the emir said. "The way to the land of the Fire Worshipers is long. Only a few of our older warriors know the way."

Hassan's men shrank back in the shadows, but they said, "How can you ask us to abandon your son? Do not our families feed on his gifts? Has he not led us to riches in many raids? We cannot leave him. But because of your sorrow we will ask him to change his plans."

"Very well," said Serhan. "See that he does."

In the morning, Hassan, ready for the journey, appeared with all his men before the emir's tent. Hassan's oldest warrior spoke against the journey, and the other men joined him.

Hassan said, "I will go."

"Then we will go with you," said the warriors.

Serhan pushed into the center of the armed men. He raised his voice and it thundered in the crowd. Men fell back from him. "Whoever leaves with my son will have his head chopped from his shoulders by the Fire Worshipers," he shouted. "That is the reward you will get for this journey. It is impossible."

Hassan's men said, "If he goes, we go, even if our heads go."

From the edge of the crowd, Shamma begged her son not to go. "If you love us, do not begin this impossible journey. Your father and I have seen enough trouble. Give us peace."

The men made ready their horses. The warriors of the emir surrounded them. Hassan stood in their midst. In the outer circle of the older warriors was Abu Zaid, greatest warrior of Hilal.

Serhan saw him and called, "Abu Zaid, tell my son to turn back. Tell him that this raid is impossible. You have been to the land of the Fire Worshipers."

"For the young, nothing is impossible," Abu Zaid said. "I cannot say that it is impossible. I do not know that."

Hassan looked at the older warriors who surrounded his men,

and he loosened his sword in its case. One word and brother would kill brother in the Tribe of Hilal.

"You said it is impossible," Hassan said to his father. "Abu Zaid will not say it is impossible. What does impossible mean?"

Hassan called forward his youngest rider, a dark beardless youth who had already proved himself worth ten older men. "Here is a boy younger than I. He has a javelin. Would you say it is impossible for this boy to match Abu Zaid with the javelin?"

Old and young Hilalies murmured, "Clearly it is impossible. No one matches Abu Zaid with the javelin."

Abu Zaid grinned, "Now I say that this is impossible. This child, who seems a slave's son, could never match me."

"We will see," Hassan said. "Pick a target and throw, Abu Zaid."

"Don't be foolish, boy."

"Pick a target, Abu Zaid," Hassan repeated.

And all of the others murmured, "Pick a target. Show this boy that the impossible cannot be done."

"Hassan should learn this at a cost to himself," Abu Zaid said. He pointed to a camel almost one hundred yards away. "There stands Hassan's favorite camel. Now watch!"

Abu Zaid hurled his javelin. It whistled through the air and quivered in the neck of Hassan's camel. The camel fell dead.

"Learn, O Hassan," said Abu Zaid.

"Match him," Hassan ordered the dark youth.

Beside the fallen camel stood one of the finest animals in

Abu Zaid's herd, a white Naka. Hardly seeming to aim, the boy threw his javelin. It flashed against the bright sky, and Abu Zaid's camel dropped heavily as the javelin's steel point cleanly pierced his neck.

The warriors murmured in amazement, for among all of Bani Hilal only Abu Zaid had ever thrown the javelin so far. The women laughed and said, "Abu Zaid will furnish the meat for feasting tonight."

Abu Zaid grew very angry. "See if he can match me on a

target that moves," he said. "Any woman can kill a standing camel."

Abu Zaid threw a second javelin, and it pierced a hawk that was circling over the camp. But before the bird had fallen to the ground, the boy hurled his second javelin. It struck the hawk forcefully and lay beside the javelin of Abu Zaid, touching it.

"Has he matched you?" Hassan asked.

"Yes," growled Abu Zaid. "But he would not be alive now if he had tried to better me."

"You have seen the impossible done," said Hassan. "We can do it again in the land of the Fire Worshipers. Do you worry now, Father, when the youngest of our raiders has equaled Abu Zaid?"

"Truly, it is amazing," said Emir Serhan. "Boy, what is your name?"

"Diab ben Gannim, sire."

"Go, if you must," said Emir Serhan to Hassan. "This is a day for marvels. Surely, Diab ben Gannim, your javelin has the power of the jinni."

Diab ben Gannim said, "That is true, sire. Once thrown, my javelin is fated always to strike flesh. On the day it does not, I will die. So my mother, who could cut the sands and see into the future, told me."

"May that day never come," said Emir Serhan.

As the raiders moved their horses out of the camp, Shamma came to the horse of her son Hassan. "Please do not go," she said.

"I must."

"Then let me send more men and arms with you," Shamma pleaded.

"By the strength of my own sword, the spear of Diab, and the bravery of my own men I shall raid and win," said Hassan.

"Then take this necklace," said Shamma. "It was my mother's gift to me. It is the most precious thing I own, and once it was lost. When it was found, I found your father."

Hassan took the necklace and placed it inside his cloak. The warriors moved out of the station and onto the ridges of the dunes. Shamma watched their shadows grow long and thin and finally disappear as the raiders rode down the great hills of sand.

When they were one day along the march, Hassan spoke to his men, "All those who want to go back can do so now."

"We go with you," the men said. "If you win, we rejoice. If you lose, we stand by you."

Diab ben Gannim said, "We will not lose."

News reached Queen Kherma that Hassan was going to the land of the Fire Worshipers. With her ministers and court she traveled across the sands until they met the raiders. She sent her ministers forward to talk to Hassan.

"We bring you arms and men and thanks from Queen Kherma," they said.

"I accept the thanks," Hassan said, "but it should wait until we win. I need no arms and men from your gracious queen. This I do myself."

The ministers rode back to Queen Kherma. "How can I get

this noble lord of Bani Hilal to accept help?" she asked her wisest minister.

"Bear him the gifts yourself," the minister advised her.

With her face covered, Kherma approached Hassan. "Why do you refuse my gifts? I cannot see you fight for my brother without help. I too have pride. I must do something."

"I have refused help from my own father and mother," said Hassan. "How can I take it from you? It is reward enough to serve you."

Kherma let fall her veil, and her beautiful face was revealed to Hassan. She was turned so that only he could see it. "I shall send men and order them to follow you at a distance. They will give help if need arises. This I do for more reasons than my brother. If any harm came to you, I would not wish to live."

Hassan could not refuse. He could not speak. She covered her face again, and he marched off with his men. The warriors of Queen Kherma strung out behind Hassan's soldiers on the plain. As he rode, Hassan remembered his mother's necklace. It is worth a kingdom, he thought. I will send it to her as a gift. This will more than pay for the men and soldiers she sends. Hassan called his servant and sent the necklace back to the queen.

Queen Kherma was astounded at the beauty of the jewels. I cannot refuse it, she thought. If I do he might refuse the men I send, and harm might come to him. He must return. By this necklace I know he will return to me.

To reach the land of the Fire Worshipers, Hassan's raiders had to cross a desert so hot that where its sands touched the sea the water boiled. The hot dunes of the desert ran like great white fingers out into the sea. On either side of the fingers of sand were bays of boiling water. Long was the journey through this desolation. Sweet water there was none. All was hot and tasted of the sea. Men died of thirst. The bones of horses bleached on the white sand. Even the camels weakened and had to be unloaded. It was too hot to travel by day. At night, clouds of steam rose from the boiling sea, and the men were often lost.

Each time that the raiders came to the sea they had to travel inland along the fingers of sand to where the bay ended and land began again. Gradually the last of the sweet water was used. But each night's travel brought only more bays, and more long journeys back to the land; the country of the Fire Worshipers was still far distant, and men, horses, and camels were dying.

From afar Shamma felt the suffering of her son. Her face burned from the air of the desert through which Hassan marched, and her head and eyes ached from staring into the sun through her son's eyes. She could not sleep at night but, like her son out on the desert of the boiling sea, she had to march up and down the tent. Often Serhan spoke to her, but never was she comforted.

"If he had obeyed me," Serhan told her, "I would have given him my ancestor's wooden sword. The sword of Kuleib."

"A wooden sword," scoffed Shamma. "What good would that be, my husband? Our son needs the finest steel."

"This sword is enchanted," said Serhan. "But I would not wish to lose it because of the foolish wish of a boy."

Shamma said, "Perhaps I will sleep."

She lay down and began to breathe heavily. Thinking his wife was asleep, Serhan slept. As soon as he was asleep, Shamma rose and searched the tent for the enchanted sword. When she found it, she stole away in the night and called a messenger of her tribe.

"Take this to Queen Kherma," she said, giving him the sword. "Tell her to send it to my son wherever he is. I know he is somewhere on a hot desert because I feel his sorrow on my own brow."

The messenger galloped away to the Yemen with the enchanted sword. Help was on its way to Hassan. And he needed it.

Shamma was not satisfied with sending the enchanted sword. One day she met Abu Zaid as he was out exercising his horse on the plain. He spoke to her with the respect that was due a queen. But she scarcely looked at him.

"Why do you turn your head from me?" he asked her.

"I had not noticed you," Shamma said. "My thoughts were out with the men."

"Am I not a man?" asked Abu Zaid.

"You are an old man," said the queen. "I was thinking of the young and strong men who are out fighting. Of Hassan, young enough to be your son. And of Diab ben Gannim, the young man who bested you with the javelin. They are probably winning great victories now, while you play boys' games with your horse."

"They can win no victories that I cannot win," said Abu Zaid angrily.

"Do you prove that by riding up and down this empty plain?" asked Shamma. "At what enemy are you shaking your javelin and waving your sword now? At jackals or vultures or tamarisk trees? You were willing enough to encourage the boys to go off on the long raid."

"*Ya Hai!*" cried Abu Zaid. "I will show you who plays at boys' games. I ride with my men today to rescue those boys."

Abu Zaid wheeled his horse and galloped back toward his tents. As she watched him, Shamma's heart was glad. The greatest warrior of the Bani Hilal was going to join her son in his hour of need.

Hassan and his men lay on the edge of the burning sand. Across a narrow bay were palm trees and the green of an oasis. Yet they could not reach the water and the dates and the shade, for a boiling sea lay between them. The journey back around the bay would be too long.

Through cracked lips Hassan said, "Here it seems we die. In sight of Paradise, but on this side of the water."

Near evening a rider appeared across the sand. He came swiftly, and soon he reined in his camel beside the fallen men.

He handed the enchanted sword to Hassan, and though Hassan had never seen the sword, he had heard his father, the emir, talk of its marvelous powers. With sword in hand, Hassan approached the boiling sea. He touched the waves and they split aside. He led his men and the men of Queen Kherma across to the palm gardens and wells of water that seemed to drain from the honey hives of bees.

The messenger on the swift camel returned to Yemen with news of Hassan's safety. Two women were joyful at that news, and bonfires were lighted in Yemen and in the land of Bani Hilal.

Beyond the garden where honey water came from the wells there were alabaster towers and the glitter of golden walls. There was a great and enchanted city full of treasure where all men slept. Hassan led his men to the walls, seeking food. He knocked on the gate with his javelin. The head of a terrible *rasad* appeared above the gate. "Fall back or die," thundered the *rasad*. "I am only the keeper of the outer gate. Inside are hundreds, more terrible than I."

"Why do you bar the way?" cried Hassan.

"We do the will of our master, the king, and we must guard his treasure while the city sleeps," roared the *rasad*. "Now fall back or die."

"What is the name of your master?" cried Hassan.

"Tubba, who was fought by Rizk, son of Kuleib."

"He is my ancestor," said Hassan. "I bear his enchanted sword. Make way. I enter."

"Knock with the sword on the gate," said the *rasad*. "If it opens inward, you may enter this city. If it opens outward I will come forth and kill you all."

Hassan hesitated only an instant. Then he knocked. The gate began to creak, for it had long been shut. Then it began to swing. And it swung inward. Hassan and his men poured inside the golden walls. The *rasad*, huge and ugly, bowed down and led them to buildings of marble, gold, and ivory, with windows made of clearest crystal.

The men were wild with delight. Diab ben Gannim hacked a great piece of gold from the corner of a building.

"Again with Hassan we win!" they shouted. "A fortune is ours."

"Take nothing," Hassan ordered them. "We rest here and go on with only what we need to rescue Queen Kherma's brother. That is water, food, camels, and weapons. We will take nothing until we return with our mission fulfilled."

The men were silent and ashamed. They began to search the palace armory for the sharpest spears and swords. They took no gold.

Beyond the alabaster city, dark mountains guarded the way to the land of the Fire Worshipers. In these mountains were wild tribesmen who fought Hassan and his men for every pebble and grain of earth. There was no thorn bush for the camels to eat, and many of them died. No grass grew from the black rock, and the horses sickened. The hillmen poured down arrows and stones from the mountainsides. And with each hill and

valley the army of the enemy grew. Their tall pikes were like trees along the ridge line.

Hassan was wounded. Without horses or camels, his men carried him into a deep valley. His faithful few guarded the pass and fought the hillmen back.

"Find a rock that will not move, no matter how hard my back presses against it," Hassan ordered his men. "Stand me against the rock. There I will fight until I join the good men who have died following me."

Hassan's men placed him against a mighty boulder. He raised his sword and waited. At the mouth of the pass Diab ben Gannim cut down the hillmen as fast as they appeared.

"They do not seem to be many separate men," called Diab. "They seem like one monster with many heads."

But finally the surging human tide broke past Diab and swept on toward Hassan. Against the rock Hassan stood and swung his sword in great arcs. But still the hillmen came. Diab ben Gannim disappeared in the fight. The hillmen pressed so hard against Hassan that he was forced to one knee. But he fought on, knowing he would die.

And then a cry thundered through the mountain passes, and the sound of swordplay was stilled for a moment. "Abu Zaid!" was the cry in the mountains. "Abu Zaid the Hilali has come."

Into the pass came Abu Zaid, riding down the hillmen, cutting through them so cleanly that his sword rang on the rocks on either side of the pass. Nothing could stand against the fury of the great warrior's attack. The mountain men were beaten and scattered.

The city of the Fire Worshipers was on the plain below the mountain. With only one day of rest Abu Zaid and Hassan moved down on the city. Looking at the stout walls, Abu Zaid said, "We are too weak to break through the walls. We are too few to frighten them into surrender. I will fight their king."

And so the challenge went up to the city of Fire Worshipers, and the king accepted. That night a Hilali scout entered the city with gold and talked with the old men in the bazaar who knew all secrets. To Abu Zaid the scout brought this news: "Their king is protected by a jinni. He can not be killed in battle by a horseman. That is why he accepts."

"Fear not," said Abu Zaid. "I will defeat him and his jinni."

The next morning, the soldiers of the Fire Worshipers marched out on the plain. The Hilalies kept back in the rocks on the hillside so that the Fire Worshipers would not know how few opposed them. Abu Zaid rode out before the Hilalies. The king rode out in front of his Fire Worshipers. The Fire Worshipers were silent. From the Hilalies came no sound.

The king lowered his lance and charged.

Abu Zaid stepped down from his horse and gave the reins to Diab ben Gannim.

The Fire Worshipers muttered. The Hilalies cried out. The king stopped his charge, and pulled up his horse. "Mount again, you desert savage," he cried at Abu Zaid.

"I need no horse to fight you," cried Abu Zaid.

"Mount or I'll ride you into the dirt."

"Fight, if you have the heart for it," shouted Abu Zaid.

The king charged. His great lance seemed to go right through the body of Abu Zaid. But still he leaped toward the king. Horse and rider fell in a great cloud of dust.

Out of the dust rose Abu Zaid with the king of the Fire Worshipers held helpless in his grip. With Diab fighting at his back, Abu Zaid dragged the king back to the hillside. "Come no further," he cried to the soldiers, "or your king dies."

Ministers came out from the city. "What will you have of us?" they asked. "Free our great king."

Hassan set the conditions. "For me, the brother of Queen Kherma must be released. To Abu Zaid and his brave Hilalies you must give all that is light and precious in your city."

And so the Fire Worshipers began to carry out the ransom. For five days pack animals moved across the plain with the treasure. On the last day, Suleiman, brother of Queen Kherma, was freed, and the king of the Fire Worshipers was sent back to his city. The Hilalies began to move back across the mountains. This time the hillmen let them pass without trouble, for they had tasted enough of the steel of Abu Zaid and the Bani Hilal.

When they reached the enchanted city, Hassan said, "Now I will take all that is light and precious from the city of my ancestor. It will go to the wives and children of Hilal who died with me." And this was done.

On the edge of the desert Queen Kherma waited with a great

supply train. When she saw the warriors approach she said, "On this day I am twice blessed. First my brother returns. And the man who saved him also returns."

That night there was feasting. Abu Zaid asked Kherma's hand in marriage for Hassan. And the marriage was arranged.

The wedding feast surpassed all others known to the Kingdom of Yemen. All of the poor people of the land were gathered, and feasts were laid out for all men to eat. Hassan had flakes of gold poured on the food, and the poor sang out his name so loudly that it was heard by sailors far out on the sea.

In the days that followed horse races and sword games were held. Everyone blessed Hassan and his queen. And the Bani Hilal ruled the Yemen in those days.

7

THE WONDERFUL MARE KHADRA

After Hassan had lived in Yemen four years he wished to return to his tribe at Saroo. Kherma joined him, and Hassan brought her brother Suleiman along so that he would not make trouble back in Yemen, for he was a headstrong youth. A governor, old and trusted, was left to rule the Yemen.

Hassan's party approached Saroo when all the Hilalies were gathered at a great market on the plain. The chiefs and raiders raised their spears and cried out in favor of Hassan. Hassan and his queen were seated on a hill overlooking the market, and a feast was begun.

In the middle of the feast a merchant and a crier came up the hill from the market.

"Hear," the crier called. "Hear of this Arabian horse whose

name is Khadra (Green). Is she swift? She has been seen in Yemen and the Nejd on the same day. Is she strong? Hear! She once bore her master and four unhorsed warriors from the midst of battle. Oh, and she is wise. And beautiful. See from here that her neck glistens as though she wears jewels. See her head high there, and the shine of her eyes."

Hassan and all the Hilalies shouted at the merchant, "Bring the horse before us."

Games and swordplay stopped and all gathered to see the wondrous mare. The crier again began to shout:

"Her sire was Seif. His sire was Hatheck. His sire was . . ." The crier told of the whole family of the wonderful horse, Khadra the Mare. "Behold!" he cried.

One horse was on the plain; one sun in the sky. Khadra's darkness moved over the plain that had gone fresh and light green from the rain. She stretched forth her forelegs, and her hind legs flowed forward. One wave ran over her muscles like rain moving across sea swells. Her mane spread out like gay pennants unfurled. When her feet touched the earth they were like the skilled hands of two drummers beating perfect time. The men watching her seemed to hear the sound of drums.

"*Ya Allah!*" called the bravest riders of the *gom*. "We can look at her no longer."

They stared away into the blue depths of the sky while Khadra cavorted on the plain. Never had they seen deeper into the water of heaven, for while Khadra moved no cloud or wave of wind stirred there.

"I will buy her," shouted Hassan. "If it takes all of the gold in Yemen, I will have her. Of such horses of the Hilal I have dreamed these past four years."

Hassan sent an adviser to the crier and the merchant. The adviser offered one hundred measures of gold and one hundred camels for the mare Khadra. For offering such a great price the Hilali warriors cheered Hassan.

"Here is a man who truly loves a good horse," they shouted.

But the crier and the merchant laughed at Hassan's offer. The crier shouted, "That is a fine price, but it is far less than the price of the mare Khadra."

The Hilalies murmured, "Less than the price. What can these madmen want?"

Abu Zaid came into the crowd and pushed toward the crier and the merchant. "I offer two hundred measures of gold, two hundred slaves, and two hundred camels."

"*Marha!* Hurray!" shouted the Hilalies. "No one is more generous than Abu Zaid. No one more truly loves a fine horse. *Marha! Marha!*"

The merchant shook his head. The crier shouted, "The price is too low."

"Too low!" shouted Abu Zaid. "Merchant, you are a fool! Is the horse a jinni perhaps? I see here only a horse, though a beautiful one."

The crowd was very excited. The younger men threw their javelins into the air. The older ones thumped the ground with their lances until the earth shook underfoot. Bakir, a man most

skilled of all the tribe in buying and stealing horses, was brought forward to talk down the value of Khadra. The sharp tongue of Bakir could make the proudest owner of the finest horse hang his head in shame.

"Speak to the mad crier and merchant," the crowd urged Bakir. "Find the faults of this horse."

As Bakir watched Khadra his mean eyes widened and then shone. He started to speak. But he could say nothing. He could only watch Khadra.

One of the servants of Diab ben Gannim heard the bargaining in the market. He pushed through the crowd and saw the wonderful mare Khadra. I must tell my master about this horse, he thought. He ran off toward the desert where Diab was hunting.

When he heard of Khadra, Diab turned his horse from the hunt and galloped into the market. Diab roared through the crowd and flung himself down beside Khadra. He stroked the fine legs of the mare. He looked into her eyes and mouth. He checked her strong barrel and felt her shoulders and forelegs. "Whose mare was this?" he asked the crier.

"I will not give the name," said the crier, "but it belonged to a man of great wealth. When he died, none of his family could ride such a horse as this. I was commissioned to sell it. Except by the will of God that took the master's life, this mare would never be sold."

Diab sent his servants to his tents to bring all of his wealth to the plain. On the ground of the market place the wealth of

Diab was assembled — three hundred she-camels, two hundred horses, three hundred necklaces, three hundred richly decorated shields, swords and daggers, three hundred measures of gold, and one thousand dinars.

"Take them," said Diab. "I will have this priceless mare Khadra."

The crier and the merchant talked long together. At last the crier announced to the crowd, "You have spoken truly. This mare is priceless. These trifles will not buy her."

"*Yoa-eeh!*" screamed the crowd.

Diab tore out his sword and jumped across his goods to seize the merchant and the crier. He laid his sword along the necks of both men. "I will take this mare at all costs. Do you understand me?"

"Good," said the merchant. "The mare Khadra is yours. Our master has so instructed us: 'Give this mare only to him who is willing to take her at the edge of the sword. For only a man of such spirit is worthy of being master to such a horse.' "

Diab himself led the mare from the market place while the crowd talked long about it. At once Diab hired the greatest groom in the tribe to care for Khadra. Diab had no more wealth and scarcely enough to buy shelter and food for Khadra. But Diab ben Gannim was happy.

Emir Hassan and Abu Zaid were not happy. Abu Zaid muttered, "Is Diab better than we are? How could that boy get anything so priceless as the mare Khadra?"

"He won by rashness," said Hassan. "To the others it seems that we did not love the horse enough to risk all."

Abu Zaid pounded the earth with his spear. "I would have risked everything. But Diab moved too quickly. Will he always move that quickly?"

And so discord came among the three great heroes of Hilal, for Abu Zaid and Hassan were jealous of Diab's beautiful mare. But Diab was a young man. He did not care that the older men of Hilal were angry. Each day he rode by the tent of Abu Zaid and called, "Ho, Abu Zaid, here is a horse that will make your heart sing. But it takes a young man to ride such a noble mount."

Inside the tent, the servants of Abu Zaid talked as loudly as they could to drown out the sound of Diab. But Abu Zaid heard clearly. His face grew grim, and his forehead was like the ripples in the sand when a great flood has passed over it. The day came when Abu Zaid went out on the desert in long, lonely hunts. He spoke to no one, and all men seeing him said, "There will be trouble. It sits already on the forehead of Abu Zaid. Woe to Diab ben Gannim, and his horse."

And Hassan was no happier. He had come home the wealthiest man in the tribe of Hilal. And yet he did not have the finest horse. Secretly Hassan went into the distant kingdoms, trying to buy the finest horse. Many horses were brought back to the land of Hilal. Each horse looked strong and swift and beautiful. Each horse raced against Khadra, and each was beaten. But Hassan did not admit to being the owner of the beaten horses. He had other Arabs ride the horses against Diab's Khadra. And Hassan waited for the horse that would beat Khadra.

But no horse alone could beat Khadra. One day Diab ben Gannim pranced before the assembled men of Hilal and shouted, "*Hai*, men of Hilal. Many horses have run against Khadra, but none can match her. I am tired of running her against your nags. Not wishing to take your money in useless bets, I will make you a fair offer. My Khadra will run any distance against ten of your best horses. Station your horses at points along the plain. Khadra will start behind the last horse. She will then pass each of the ten horses and run the last one into the floor of the desert."

Saying this, Diab waved at the angry Hilali warriors, and his horse pranced away for her daily race against the east wind.

"I have had enough insolence from that boy," said Abu Zaid. "I will ride all over the Nejd and raid for the swiftest horses."

"And I too," said Hassan. "I will buy five horses, and you will raid for five. Together they will ride Khadra into the desert."

And so it was arranged. Five horses would be the swiftest horses that Hassan could buy. Five horses would be the swiftest that Abu Zaid could raid from any tribe. Abu Zaid prepared to lead his *gom* out to get the swiftest horses.

"There is no man who can say that I will not risk enough to have the swiftest horse. We raid against the fierce Bani Suleym, who have the swiftest horses in the land. When I return in one month, the race will be held and I will ride the tenth horse."

The Hilali warriors worried. "Either Abu Zaid will ride Diab into the desert or he will cut him from the horse. No one challenges Abu Zaid without regretting it." Abu Zaid said nothing as he prepared for the raid.

On the plain, day was growing old and shadowed and all *wadis* were wrinkled purple veins when Abu Zaid led the long line of the *gom* out toward the land of the Bani Suleym. One by one the shadows of horses and men dropped into the dark stream of Wadi Mukra.

That night it was so hot in Saroo that no one slept. Everyone and everything — men, women, children, horses, and camels — moved restlessly in the night. All waited.

Abu Zaid raided ten horses from the Suleym. Five men riding the five slowest horses were caught and killed by the Suleym. Five men riding the five swiftest horses escaped to the Bani Hilal. Hassan paid a fortune and bought five swift steeds. It was said that one was brought in from across the sea.

On the day of the race, the ten horses were stationed out along the plain. Diab ben Gannim sat on Khadra and joked with the maidens of the tribe. He noticed that Abu Zaid rode out fully armed.

"Eh, old man," he called, "better leave that useless weight behind. That nag you ride needs every advantage."

Abu Zaid did not even look at Diab, but rode out to his last station in the desert, wearing his sword and carrying his javelin.

Jazieh, sister of Hassan and most beautiful of all Hilali maidens, called to Diab, "Be careful. Death sits on Abu Zaid's brow."

Diab laughed and made Khadra dance so that the ladies applauded. Diab smiled and waved to them, and the maidens sighed as he rode out to the starting line.

"Ready," called an old tribesman at the starting line.

Diab spoke to Khadra and she tensed as though she meant to spring across the desert in one bound.

"Fly!" shouted the starter.

Diab did not have to touch Khadra. She heard the signal and

flew forward. The first horse sprang out of his starting place and the race was on.

Though the first horse ran well, Khadra moved steadily up. Diab seemed to be holding Khadra back. Her muscles seemed to knot against the restraint. When they reached the second horse, Diab reined in. The second horse started and Khadra quickly came even with her and ran that way to the third horse. So Diab and Khadra rode down the next five horses. When they started with the eighth horse the crowd murmured.

"Surely even Khadra cannot continue to run like that," they said. "Hassan's swift foreign horse waits at the ninth place; and Abu Zaid's at the tenth."

At the ninth place Hassan readied his horse. Khadra came swinging into the ninth station and Hassan moved his horse out. The horse shot forward with such speed and fury that Hassan was almost unseated. She ran right away from Khadra.

Running far in front, Hassan turned in his saddle to look at Diab. Poor, proud Diab, thought Hassan, your Khadra has tired, and there is still one horse yet to race. But while Hassan was still staring behind him, Khadra and Diab flashed by, and Hassan's mare reared in frenzy. Never had horse or rider passed her.

The horses thundered into the tenth station and there Abu Zaid waited. He and Diab started at the same time. At first the horse of Bani Suleym seemed to pull away. Then Diab's horse came even. The horse of the Suleym found new speed and began to run, but Khadra ran with her. They raced along, and for

a while, Abu Zaid felt sure that his horse would break Khadra.

But suddenly he noticed that the back of Diab was to him, and his mare was losing ground. Seizing his sword, Abu Zaid made a mighty sweep at Diab's back, but the swift Khadra pulled right out from under the blow. Readying his javelin, Abu Zaid threw it at Diab's back.

Easily, Khadra raced ahead of the javelin, and it dropped to the ground in her dust. Instead of stopping, Diab, laughing and shouting, rode on deeper into the desert. He heard no sound but the wind of his passing, and he had no thoughts, but only joy at flying along on Khadra. He ran right away from where Abu Zaid had reined in his Suleym mare.

Diab rode on, but soon his joy turned to sadness, for he had nothing to run his wonderful mare against. Far across the desert he saw a white puff as a gazelle threw up her tail and began to run.

"After it!" shouted Diab ben Gannim.

They sped across the plain and toward the hills that were now creased with the coming of night. Along the foot of the slope ran the gazelle, but Khadra drew nearer. The gazelle turned this way and that, throwing up sand that glittered in the dying sun. Khadra made each turn and came on. Finally, right at the foot of the hill, the gazelle dropped, and the chase was over.

In the last faint light of evening Diab returned to the Hilali camp, riding Khadra tall and proud against the darkening sky. The camp was quiet because both the Emir Hassan and Abu Zaid sat silently within their tents.

"What?" called Diab. "Will there not be a feast to celebrate the great victory of Khadra?"

But no one answered him, and the old men of the tribe shook their heads. The fortunetellers cut the sands and the sands told of trouble — trouble among the greatest of Bani Hilal.

8

THE BANISHMENT OF DIAB

Diab, because he was young, forgot about the envy and anger of the great men of Bani Halil. Abu Zaid, who was a warrior and raider, also forgot his grudge against Diab. But Hassan, the emir, could not forget. He waited for a chance to even the score with Diab ben Gannim, and the chance came soon because of a woman.

Diab when a young man had married a woman of humble station who bore him two fine sons, Murshid and Mahmoud. Later the mother of Murshid and Mahmoud died of fever while Diab was away riding with the *gom*. For a long time Diab had wished a mother for his fine sons and a wife whose beauty would match his fame as a warrior. There was only one woman fit for this and she was Jazieh, beautiful sister of Emir Hassan, but because of his humble birth Diab had never spoken to Hassan about this matter. Yet Diab's fame as a warrior grew; the prowess of his great mare Khadra became a legend; and through raids Diab soon became a rich man again, despite the fantastic price he had paid for Khadra. And the day came when Diab summoned his courage and rode with some of his men to the tents of Emir Hassan.

One of Diab's men addressed the men of the emir, "My leader, Diab ben Gannim, has come to ask something of the great Emir Hassan."

Hassan, who heard these words, turned directly to Diab. "Speak," he said. "What is it that you want?"

Fierce with love and worry, Diab spoke: "I want the hand of your sister Jazieh in marriage."

The emir stared at Diab ben Gannim. Though he was a just man, Hassan could not forget that Diab owned the greatest horse of all Hilal. He was angered by Diab's fierce and insolent demand.

"I will think about it," he said at last. He did not look at Diab.

Diab, whose only desire in life now was Jazieh, was angry. "Think hard about it, my prince," he said coldly.

"Go," said the emir. "I will give you my answer when it is ready."

On the next day, Diab and his party appeared before the tents of Hassan.

"What do you wish now?" asked Hassan's men.

"The same thing I wished before," said Diab. "I want to take Jazieh as my wife."

"We will ask the emir for his decision," they said.

Hassan told his men, "Send Diab away. I will give him my answer in a letter."

When Diab heard this, he growled, but he turned back to his tents.

After Diab had gone, Hassan told his men, "The letter can be brief. Make it one word — no. But if he asks, give him reasons. Jazieh is too young. Her mother does not wish her to marry yet."

"But what if he does not accept that answer?" asked Hassan's men. "Diab will say that Jazieh is not too young to be a wife."

"Then tell him Jazieh is too young to be a widow," said Hassan. "He is brave but he is foolhardy. One day soon he will be killed."

"And if he refuses to accept that reason?"

"Then remind him he is no prince of Bani Hilal," said Hassan. "He is a slave's son with a strong arm and a swift horse. I made him a warrior. I can make him tend goats and sheep. Tell him to marry another humble woman."

When Diab read the letter and forced Hassan's men to give reasons, he was so angry that the messengers barely escaped alive.

"Hassan plots against me," said Diab. "He thinks there will be no more war in the Nejd and that he will not need me as a warrior. Well, I will show him about herding sheep and goats. I will herd his cattle and sheep right away from him."

Diab and three of his raiders moved that night against the camel herds of Emir Hassan. They rounded up the young ones and drove them away. When they were almost back to their land, Sa'ad, the younger brother of Hassan, caught up with them and tried to take the camels back. Though he did not want to hurt the boy, Diab was so angry that he knocked Sa'ad from his horse, hurting him badly.

The news of Sa'ad's injury was brought to Hassan, and great was his anger. "I will drive Diab ben Gannim from the Nejd, or kill him. Get ready to ride after him."

But no warrior readied his horse. Some of them liked Diab ben Gannim and wished him no harm. Others hated Diab but they wished no harm to themselves. They feared his swift javelin and heavy sword. Hassan said, "Where are the men of my *gom?* Who obeys the orders of his emir?"

No warrior spoke, but at that moment Abu Zaid rode into the camp with a party of hunters.

"Here is Abu Zaid," cried the warriors. "He will know what to do. Should we fight against Diab and his men?"

"What have they done?" asked Abu Zaid.

Hassan told him.

"Diab has wronged his emir," said Abu Zaid. "He must be punished. Fill my water bag and I will lead the *gom* against Diab ben Gannim."

Three great battles were fought against the warriors of Diab.

After the first one Diab escaped with one hundred men. After the second one he had only twenty. In the third battle only Diab, because of the swiftness of Khadra, escaped. The Bani Hilal searched every cave and hill in the Nejd. Finally a *gom* found Khadra lame and tired outside a cave. Inside, Diab was sleeping. He had been wounded many times, so that his clothes were stuck to him with blood. They bound Diab with strong ropes, then they blindfolded him, and brought him before Hassan.

"What will you do with him?" they asked Hassan. "He has wronged you."

"If I had met him battle I would have killed him," said Hassan. "Now he is no hero. He is but a tired wounded thief. For his fate we must ask Budair."

Diab's crimes were told to Budair. No one appeared to say a word for Diab, because all his men had been driven from the Nejd.

"Nothing good has been said for him," said Budair. "Therefore he must die."

The judge and all the warriors of Bani Hilal were sad to see Diab die, but they prepared to execute him. The warriors gave him his last request: "Do you want food and water so that you may die strong?"

"None," said Diab. "But I do not wish to die blind. Let me have light."

The blindfold was taken from Diab's eyes. He looked around at all the nobles and warriors of Hilal and saw Abu Zaid among them. Abu Zaid was a great fighter like himself. To him, Diab cried, "Abu Zaid, I am yours. Save me."

Diab did not remind Abu Zaid that he had once saved him in battle, but Abu Zaid sprang to his feet. "Forgive him," Abu Zaid said to Hassan. "I will speak for him from now on."

Hassan had no choice. He did not wish to lose the two greatest warriors of his tribe by one execution. "So be it," he said to Diab. "You are spared because of Abu Zaid and your past bravery. Come now and eat at my table as a sign that all is forgiven and forgotten."

So Diab was seated at the table of Hassan. But during the meal he saw Jazieh pass the tent, and his anger returned at the sight of her beauty. She would never be his, though he had earned her a thousand times. And she loved him. Of that he was certain. Still he could say nothing. He choked on his food and waited for the dinner to be over. Diab wanted Jazieh, as Hassan had wanted Khadra. As long as Jazieh was not his, Diab's thoughts would be dark.

Diab left the tents of Emir Hassan and rode deep into the desert to seek his men. He found them scattered in the wilds of the Nejd. Some were dying of thirst in the desert. Others lay starving and wounded in dark caves of the Great Wilderness. Some had been captured and were the slaves of other tribes. Diab nursed the wounded, fed the hungry, gave the thirsty water and milk, and bought or raided away the men who were slaves.

"How can we pay you for this?" asked his men. "We were

dead and now we are alive and on swift horses. We carry fine arms. What can we do for you, Diab?"

"The day of payment will come," promised Diab. "Now we must train and drill until we are the swiftest raiders of the Nejd."

"But who will we fight? No one could stand against us now."

"Abu Zaid," said Diab.

A shiver of fear passed through the ranks of the horsemen. But no man looked down at his saddle. "If it must be so," they said. "We will follow you against Abu Zaid."

"First, we must make ready," said Diab. "We must live without women or children. We must live in the wilds. Each dawn we will ride up the side of Jabal al-Jibal. If the horses are driven uphill always they will fly when they run on level ground. The sky will give us water. We must never live near water holes. For that is what makes men soft and peaceful. Thirst puts the devil in a warrior. Your home will be the back of your horse. You will eat only what you kill. Each day we will ride down the swiftest gazelle of the desert. By fighting for food and drink you will get ready for the battle to come."

For many months the men of Diab trained in the wilderness. Some grew so skilled with the javelin that they could pierce a hawk on the wing. Some grew so fierce that they would face a lion without arms. At the dawn of every day they drove their horses up the flinty sides of Jabal al-Jibal. They learned to ride for days with no food and little water. Diab gave prizes to those who could ride the longest without meat, drink, or rest. The men of Diab became the fiercest raiders ever to move on the desert.

Diab did not depend on drill alone. When he raided the Bani Hilal to take Jazieh, he wished to be certain of victory. One day he went all alone to Jabal al-Shaytan (Devil Mountain). There lived a fierce jinni who drank the blood of warriors and carried away the fairest maidens. Standing before a hole in the ground Diab called, "Ho, jinni, child of evil. Come out and hear what I offer you."

The head and shoulders of the jinni appeared above the ground. The shoulders of the jinni were wider than Diab was tall. "*Hai,* little warrior," thundered the jinni. "You must be a madman to come to my home and shout at me. I'll drink your blood here and now."

"I have no blood," said Diab. "The sun has boiled it all away. Hear what I propose! Because I am a child of darkness myself I have great powers. My javelin, once thrown, is fated always to strike flesh and bone."

"Except," interrupted the jinni, "on the day it does not strike flesh and bone. Then you die. I know the power of darkness. It is never perfect. Always there is one thing wrong with it. Well, what do you want of me? And what can you give?"

"I may have to fight great Abu Zaid himself," said Diab. "Against such a warrior I must have every favor the powers of darkness can give. I wish to be protected, so that my blood cannot be shed by Abu Zaid."

"That I can do," said the jinni, "but what can you do for me? Your request is small because you have so little blood."

"In exchange I will bring to you the most beautiful and perfect female of her kind. If she is not the most perfect of her kind may I die for it."

"Agreed," said the jinni. "For such a female I will give you protection. I can promise you that your blood will never be shed by any man in whose veins there is blood different from yours. Even I could not break this protection and shed your blood."

"Very well, jinni," said Diab. "Say the words and lay on the protective charm."

"First the woman," answered the jinni. "How do I know you have such a beauty?"

"I have her in my camp now," Diab said. "Say the words and I will bring her to you."

Diab and the jinni argued loud and long over who would fill his part of the bargain first. Finally the jinni said, "Very well. You are in my power anyway, for if you fail to bring her and if she is not the most beautiful of all, you will die anyway. Sit on the rock there with your back to me. It is not permitted that you see how I make the charm."

Diab sat on the rock with his back to the jinni. He heard the muttering of a strange tongue, the beat of birds' wings and the sound of an owl. Then there was smoke all around him, and in the midst of it the head of the jinni appeared to be floating.

"Go!" the jinni thundered. "Bring the most wondrous female. You are protected."

"There is one thing I must tell you," said Diab. "I have promised only to bring the female to you. I am not responsible if she stays with you. That is up to you."

"Hai!" shouted the jinni. "Do not speak foolishness. She will stay. If she takes one step away from my side I can paralyze her two legs so that she can run no further. Bring her."

Diab went straightway to the foot of Jabal al-Shaytan and untied Khadra from a bush. He led the beautiful mare up the slope to the jinni.

"What is this?" thundered the jinni. "You promised me the most beautiful woman of her kind — not a horse."

"I promised you the most beautiful female of her kind. And I have kept my bargain," said Diab. "This is the most beautiful of all mares. Can you say differently?"

The jinni thundered and raged, but he could not deny that Diab had filled his part of the bargain. Finally the jinni was less angry because he saw that Khadra was indeed the most beautiful of all horses. Still he bellowed at Diab, "Very well. But before you laugh at me, remember our bargain. I protected you only from having your blood shed by one whose blood is different from yours. There are many ways that you can die. And I will keep your horse, and never let her free."

Diab walked away down the mountainside, well pleased with the bargain. He knew that Khadra would never stay with the ugly jinni. That night, when feeding time came, Khadra would come back to the camp of Diab, and the jinni would have nothing.

When night came, Diab prepared food for Khadra, just as though she were still in the camp. In the mountains Khadra began to steal slowly away from the cave of the jinni. At the last minute the jinni awoke with a great roar that shook the trees, and he paralyzed two of Khadra's legs.

But Khadra was not a woman. She still managed to hobble away. Once away from the sound of the jinni's bellowing, power returned to her legs and she ran back to the camp of Diab.

"I have outwitted the jinni," said Diab. "Tomorrow we raid the Hilalies. We must ride this night."

Diab waved his arm and the long line of fierce and bearded warriors swung their horses in behind Khadra and galloped toward the land of the Hilalies.

At dawn Diab led his men to the edge of a great *wadi*. At the bottom of the *wadi* grazed the most beautiful camels of Bani Hilal, the camels of Emir Hassan and Abu Zaid. While the sun drenched the crumbling sides of the *wadi* with the blood of dawn, Diab sent scouts to drive off the camels. He and most of his men waited and watched. The long line of camels began to move up the *wadi*. Their strings of bells made a soft, tinkling sound.

"The fruit of our first raid is great," said Diab to his men.

But as Diab and his men turned away from the edge of the

wadi, they were attacked by Miree, the brother of Emir Hassan, who was returning from a hunt. *"Hai,"* shouted Miree. "It is Diab and his robbers. Kill all of them."

Diab's men might all have been killed, for Miree and his men attacked strongly and two of Diab's men were cut down on the crest of the *wadi.* Miree rolled on the ground with a third raider, and soon the man was overpowered by young Miree's strong arms. But then Diab ran forward and engaged Miree in hand-to-hand combat with daggers. Thrusting strongly with his short

blade, Diab struck Miree a blow that drove him to the ground.
Miree's men, seeing their leader down and fearing the power of
Diab, rode back toward the Hilali camp.

When Emir Hassan heard of the raid and of the serious
wound to Miree he cried to the sky and tore at his clothes.
"Miree, my beloved brother. Never had I harsh words with
him. Whether he lives or dies, I will now hunt Diab ben Gannim
off the end of the earth."

The emir called Abu Zaid before him and said, "I want ev-

ery man of the Bani Hilal from here to the Wadi Ennar. Let no man shirk. All must follow me. A thousand dinars for the bloody head of Diab ben Gannim."

The warriors of the Hilal prepared to leave the camp. In a hill above the station Diab watched them and smiled. To his sword bearer, Diab said, "When they go out, I will go into the camp and take Jazieh."

Just before the *gom* left the camp, Amer, the brother of Diab himself, joined the party. Seeing him, some of the men murmured. Turning toward him, Emir Hassan said, "Why are you here? Do you not know we hunt your devilish brother?"

"That I know," said Amer. "And I know Diab has wronged our whole tribe. I ask permission to meet him in single combat. If one of us is killed there can be no blood feud left in a single family. But if the emir or Abu Zaid is killed, or if they kill Diab, a feud will take place among the Arabs which can never end."

"He speaks wisely," said Judge Budair.

"Take him," said Abu Zaid. "For Amer is a fine sword, and almost as strong as Diab himself."

"I will not take him," said Hassan. "This is my injury. And I will settle it myself. I will have Diab's blood on my own sword." Saying this, he waved his sword and the *gom* galloped out of the station.

As soon as the *gom* left the camp, Diab moved down from the hill. He stationed his men at the outer edge of the camp, and he himself walked boldly toward the pavilion of the emir.

"Jazieh," he shouted, "I have come to take you. Come out and save the search."

From her hiding place in the tent, Jazieh, who was protected by one old slave, called, "Yesterday I would have welcomed you. Then you were my love and light of my eyes. Today you are a criminal who has struck down my lovely brother Miree. I will die first."

Diab smiled and moved toward the sound of her voice. He was alone among the tents. All of the women and old men were hiding. At that moment, Amer, fully armed, appeared before the tent flap of Jazieh's pavilion.

"Brother," he said, "you will never enter this tent. Instead, you will die on the sand."

"Stand aside, little brother," said Diab. "I do not wish to stain the tent flaps of my loved one with the blood of my own brother."

"You will have to fight," said Amer. "Are you afraid of fighting in daylight? Are you only a night fighter who hides in the shadows? Come on, slave brother, if you dare."

"I will fight," shouted Diab, and threw his javelin.

Amer dodged and the javelin ripped through the tent and struck the leg of the old servant who guarded Jazieh. Diab did not know this. He saw only that his javelin had not struck flesh and bone, and he feared greatly. Remembering that the jinni had given him no protection from wounds or death at the hands of men of his own blood, he was doubly afraid.

Diab turned and would have run away, but Amer was on

him. Amer stepped, jumped in the air, and struck a great two-handed blow with his sword. Diab's side and shoulder were torn open. He fell and the sand reddened under him, filling out a dark circle. Amer stood silently over him.

"You have killed him," cried Diab's men. "You have killed your own brother."

"Take him away," said Amer, "and let him die like a wolf in the wilderness."

"Carry him to your tent," begged the men. "He cannot ride."

"Away," cried Amer, "lest Hassan catch you and bury your heads in sand."

Hoisting Diab onto Khadra, his men led the horse of their dying leader into the desert.

On the wild side of Jabal al-Jibal, Diab was laid on the flinty ground. Around him, his men mounted watch, waiting for him to die. He bled no more, seeming dry of life. He burned and raved and beat his head on the hard hillside. Still, for the first day he lived.

Two days passed and Diab still lived. All marveled. He had no cover but the cold stars. He had no medicine but cold water from a mountain spring. Yet, after four days, his men knew that he would live.

For many days Diab lay silent and pale, all the fire having left him with the passing of his fever. Rocks were rolled up to shade him from the sun, and he lay in the great heat and was silent. A day came when he called his men to him.

"I have done wicked things," he said. "I have fought my own

tribe and harmed my own king. I do now repent. You should return to the tents of the Hilalies. Make the best peace you can."

"We are your men," his warriors answered. "If your quarrel goes on with Hassan, and even Abu Zaid, we stand with you. We stand with you in peace or war."

"Let there be peace," said Diab.

When Diab could ride again, he went to the tent of Abu Zaid. "I come in peace," he announced.

"*Ya Allah*, Diab, can it be you?" said Abu Zaid in disbelief. "It is believed by all that you are dead."

"That should have been," said Diab. "But I live. I wish to make peace with Emir Hassan. I wish you to take me before him and ask for pardon."

"I cannot take you as a free man," said Abu Zaid. "If Emir Hassan saw that you were standing tall he would strike you down. I must bind you and take you as a prisoner."

"As you wish," said Diab.

Abu Zaid bound Diab and led him to Hassan's tent. "I bring you a prisoner who is truly sorry," said Abu Zaid. "Forgive him. This I ask on past service to you."

Emir Hassan could not look at Diab. He choked with rage and turned away. Around the tent sat Judge Budair and the wisest and oldest counselors of the tribe. They too did not look at Diab, who was still thin and weak from his wounds. Only Diab's great dark eyes were unchanged. His once mighty wrists were like those of a child.

Turning to Budair, Emir Hassan said, "Friends, the matter is before you. I am no weak man. I could kill this man for the blood of my two brothers. I could twist his neck as he lies there, and like a desert hen he could do nothing. Instead, I ask your opinion. How will you have it?"

Judge Budair said, "O Emir Hassan, all Bani Hilal despise Diab for his crimes. He needs your kindness. You have been most wronged by him. Forgive him. Give him back his life."

Emir Hassan turned to each of the advisers. Each man nodded, "Aye, forgive him."

"Diab ben Gannim is spared," said Emir Hassan. "By my head."

Abu Zaid freed Diab from his bonds, and he knelt at Emir Hassan's feet. Looking down at him, Emir Hassan said, "Know, Diab, that pardon in these times is not easily granted. But I cannot avenge myself on a man who is already broken. Rise. We will feast on this event."

"Never again will I take up arms against you, Emir Hassan," Diab promised. "If I do, may no punishment be bad enough for me."

Criers were sent through the tents of all the station announcing that Diab had been pardoned. She-camels were killed and roasted. There was rejoicing in the tents of Hilal.

Yet it came to pass after many months that the Emir of Mecca sent to Hassan, asking for the hand of Jazieh. "The match is fitting," decided Hassan. "Make ready the bridal party."

Howdajes for travel were made ready. An armed escort was formed, carrying gay pennants on their spears. Jazieh, her slaves, and the leading women of her family were placed in their howdajes. The party left the station with the blessings of Emir Hassan and under the protection of the pick of the horsemen of Bani Hilal. Diab was not there to see the party leave.

In his tent Diab raged. He had blindfolded his eyes so he could not see the bridal party, but still he could hear their shouts and cheers. "I will raid them," he said. "I will take Jazieh by my sword."

He made ready to take his arms, but his brother Amer stopped him.

"If you take arms, I will be your first enemy — and your last," said Amer. "I'll spill your blood, brother."

"What kind of brother are you?" asked Diab. "Would you wish to see your brother die of unhappiness? That woman is my only love. Without her I die."

Amer said, "The unhappiness of one man is better than the unhappiness of the whole tribe. If you take up arms, all Bani Hilal will suffer again on your account."

"What can I do?" cried Diab.

"Go into the wilderness," said Amer, "where each man and animal lives alone, thinks only of himself, and dies alone. That is where you belong, among the wild beasts."

So Diab ben Gannim forced himself to go into the Great Wilderness to wander alone, cut off from his tribe.

9

ABU ZAID SEEKS A HORSE AND FINDS A WIFE

In the days before the Prophet Mohammed — on him be prayer and peace — brought true light to Arabia, the mightiest warriors of Bani Hilal sat in the tent of Emir Hassan, drinking from a goatskin of wine and talking of horses. Guests from the Yemen were there. Chief among the guests was Emir Suleiman of Yemen, the troublemaker, who had come to visit his brother-in-law, Emir Hassan. Suleiman, his brains dancing with mischief, boasted of his horses.

Abu Zaid drank from the goatskin and said, "No mare ever equaled Khadra, the wonderful horse of Diab ben Gannim. Khadra was the swiftest. Khadra jumped the highest and ran the longest. Truly a wonder."

"Where is this marvelous horse and her owner?" asked a Yemeni noble.

"Alas," said Budair, "Diab is in the Great Wilderness and Khadra is with him."

All the warriors sighed, thinking of Diab wandering alone and away from his tribe.

"Aye," sighed Abu Zaid. "I miss them truly. Diab was a young wolf, but there was always excitement in the tents when he was here. Now it is so dull. But you never saw such a horse."

"It is easy to boast when the horse is not here," remarked Emir Suleiman. "There is no way to prove the boasting false. But I say that Diab's horse was not the greatest. There is one greater, and her name is Heesa."

"I don't believe it," said Abu Zaid. "There was none greater than Khadra."

"I am telling the truth," said the Emir of Yemen. "I do not own this horse. Yet, the mare Heesa is the greatest of all horses. She is pure Arabian. Her owner is Prince Ja'aberie. He loves her as his own child. And truly she is as beautiful as any child. She is delicately built, with slim body and strong legs. She does not walk, she dances. She does not run, she flies. Swifter than a bird. I would bet anything that she is greater than Khadra."

"I want that mare," said Hassan. "For such a mare I would send for Diab in the Great Wilderness, just to run his Khadra into the ground. Who will go and buy her for me? I offer one hundred ordinary mares, two hundred stallions, two hundred she-camels, two thousand dinars — nay three thousand. And twenty loads of the finest silks."

The men of Yemen shook their heads. "It is not possible,"

they said. "Prince Ja'aberie would not sell her for double that amount."

"I want the mare," insisted Hassan. "Be she bought by gold or by blood." He looked all around the circle of warriors who squatted on his rugs. "Who will bring her to me?"

No man answered.

"It is just as well for your men that none are bold," said Emir Suleiman. "Heesa is protected by four slaves day and night. One of the slaves is so fierce he must surely be a child of a jinni. He takes no food for his guarding. It is said that he eats only those who come to steal the mare. I don't blame your men for showing fear."

"My men fear nothing," said Emir Hassan. "Again, who will bring Heesa to me?"

Abu Zaid looked all around the circle of brave Hilalies, and seeing no one ready to move, he stood up and bowed to Emir Hassan. "I'll bring her," he said.

"Bring her and the price I named is yours," said the emir.

Abu Zaid shook his head. "I want no price. I go for two reasons. If I bring back Heesa, you have promised to bring back Diab ben Gannim. I too would like to see the face of Diab when your wonderful mare Heesa runs Khadra into the desert."

"Very good," said Emir Hassan. "Abu Zaid, you are a true sportsman."

"And there is a second reason," said Abu Zaid. "No man must ever be able to say that a Hilali was unwilling to take great risks for his emir."

The Hilalies applauded and Suleiman was silent.

From the camp in the Nejd to the princedom of Ja'aberie was a twenty-day journey by horse, but Abu Zaid was too wise to travel by swift horse. Instead, he disguised himself with the rags of a dervish (holy man) and walked barefoot for forty days. Since he traveled slowly through the country, word of his coming did not alarm the people of Prince Ja'aberie. On the way, Abu Zaid stopped in every village to beg food. He was given scraps of food, and for this he gave advice to the villagers. So holy was his advice, no one would have thought him to be a warrior of Hilal.

Abu Zaid brought peace between two villages that had always been at war. He did this with one simple question that no man in either village could answer: "Why are you at war?" So old was the reason that no man remembered it, and when the question was asked in both villages and could not be answered, the people were ashamed and stopped fighting.

In a village of thieves Abu Zaid preached honesty. He taught this lesson well. In the night he stole all that was light and precious, even taking a jeweled pillow from under the head of the robber chief. Abu Zaid carried everything away and buried it behind a sand hill, far from the tents. In the morning, how the villagers sorrowed!

"Why has this happened to us, oh so holy man?" they asked.

"It is punishment because you are thieves," said Abu Zaid. "You are learning how others feel."

"How can we get our precious things back?"

"Swear that you will never steal again," said Abu Zaid, "and I will cut the sand" (see into the unknown) "and find them for you."

The villagers swore never to steal again and Abu Zaid recovered their goods.

The fame of Abu Zaid went everywhere before him until he reached the capital city of Ja'aberie. Entering the city he sat under a lemon tree. As he looked at the towering gates of the palace, crowds gathered around him.

"Perform some holy deed," they shouted, for they had heard that he could make gold out of lemons and move mountains with his wish.

"I will perform a wonderful deed," said Abu Zaid, "but it will be nothing easy like making gold of these lemons. Instead I will command my spirit to leave my body and go into the prince's palace."

So saying, Abu Zaid lay down in the shade and fell fast asleep.

"What will we do with him?" wondered a member of the crowd. Abu Zaid had slept many hours.

Someone said, "Let us take his body into the palace so that it will be with his spirit."

This suggestion pleased the crowd, and they carried Abu Zaid inside the palace grounds. The first part of his plan had worked very well. When nightfall came Abu Zaid awoke and found himself lying in a back garden of the palace. From behind a tamarisk tree he heard voices.

Now it so happened that the son of the vizier of Ja'aberie

loved the prince's daughter Alia. But because the vizier's son had neither wit nor courage, but only the money that his father had stolen from her father, the princess would not think of him. On the day when Abu Zaid entered the town there was great excitement, and the vizier's son had told his sister, "Tell Princess Alia to come to the gardens and I will have the holy man brought there. Then she can ask him as many questions as she wishes, away from the crowd."

"But the holy man is in the town," said his sister. "Why should Alia come to the garden?"

"Because I wish to speak to her alone," said the brother. "After you have brought her, run away."

The vizier's daughter did her brother's bidding, and Alia, not suspecting, was left alone in the dark garden. The vizier's son stepped out of his hiding place and began to talk to her. When Alia would not listen to him, the vizier's son seized her roughly, and tore off her veil.

Alia screamed, "Help me! Help me!"

Abu Zaid heard her cries and leaped from the trees to struggle with the vizier's son. The cowardly young man drew a poisoned dagger, but Abu Zaid easily avoided his thrusts and struck him down with his own short sword.

Alia ran to Abu Zaid. "You are as valiant as you are holy," she said. "I have heard great things of you. Now in my time of need you were here. What reward will you have for your valor? Speak! My father, Prince Ja'aberie, has great wealth. Ask, and be not afraid that what you ask for is too great."

"I have come for the mare named Heesa," said Abu Zaid.

"But had I known that such a prize as you were here, my aim would have been different."

"You shall have Heesa," said Alia. They walked together to the stables and Alia commanded the most bloodthirsty of the slaves to bring Heesa to Abu Zaid.

"Heesa is now yours," she said.

As Abu Zaid led the horse toward a secret gate, Alia said, "If you ever ask for another gift, I am sure that my father will give that to you, too."

"I understand," said Abu Zaid. "And perhaps I will return. But you should know that I am Abu Zaid the Hilali. I shall always serve you."

"Serve me then in this way," said Alia. "As you leave the city, stop in the main market and call out, 'I am Abu Zaid the Hilali. I have taken Heesa as a gift of Princess Alia whose honor I defended from an evil man. I killed that man, and I will kill any who follow.' Say these things so that the servants will not suffer blame. And be not afraid. There is no mare that can catch Heesa."

Abu Zaid rode Heesa into the market place. There she reared up, and he shouted to all the people as Alia had instructed him. Then he galloped out of town. Because of the speed of Heesa and the fame of Abu Zaid, no man chased him.

When Abu Zaid reached the land of the Bani Hilal he brought the mare to Emir Hassan. The emir found great joy in the sight of the beautiful mare and offered Abu Zaid riches from every land. Abu Zaid said, "I want no gifts. First you should see if you can ride this mare. Truly she is spirited."

Hassan tried to ride Heesa, but she would not have him. For three days he tried to ride her, and on the third day she pitched him to the ground and he was badly hurt.

From his bed he said to Abu Zaid, "It is no good. Heesa is your horse. I will never make her mine. You must keep her."

"I can ride her," said Suleiman. "As your brother-in-law I deserve the horse."

"Try it," said Abu Zaid.

Before Suleiman could even mount Heesa she reared high in the air and struck him on the head with her hoofs. Suleiman was carried to his tent. The horse was to stay with Abu Zaid, for no one else could ride it. But because Emir Hassan did not have the horse to race, he did not bring Diab ben Gannim back from the wilderness. Abu Zaid was happy with Heesa, sad about Diab ben Gannim, and worried about the princess. He wondered what had happened to Alia.

And this is what had happened. When the vizier's daughter found her brother's body, she ran to her father. "Alia has killed my beloved brother and your only son," she cried. "She brought this Hilali murderer here to kill him. You must go to the prince and speak against her."

When the vizier had told the story, the prince said, "I do not believe this. My daughter would never bring a murderer into her father's palace. Nor would she promise him my horse Heesa to kill your son. Bring in Alia."

Alia approached with downcast eyes. In front of all the nobles who sat on gilt chairs beside the throne, the girl was questioned. She answered, "I will not lie. I did give Heesa to Abu Zaid. But it was not promised to him beforehand. I gave it to him for saving me from the vizier's son."

"She lies to save herself," cried the vizier. "My son was good."

"Silence," commanded the prince. "Or you may have to save yourself. Your son was bad. Had he lived longer I would have had to banish him. Tell your story, Alia."

Alia told her story as it had happened. "I did not bring the Hilali inside the walls," she said.

"That is true," said one noble. "He was carried in by foolish people of the town who wished to see a marvelous trick."

A servant swore that he had seen the vizier's son hiding in the tamarisk trees waiting for Alia. Alia's maidservant said that the vizier's daughter had invited her mistress to see the holy man. Many stories were heard. The vizier's daughter lied to save her brother's name. Never had such a quarrel in high places happened in Ja'aberie's court. He was troubled because he loved his daughter and respected his vizier. Turning to the nobles, Ja'aberie said, "What is your verdict? I will abide by it."

"We must first know the truth," said one old noble. "And there is but one way to be sure that we have it. Let us send after the Hilali, Abu Zaid. If he is as brave as they say, he will come. If he is as great as they say, he will tell the truth."

Abu Zaid, riding Heesa, traveled swiftly to the court of Ja'aberie. He was not permitted to see Alia or speak to her. "Tell your story, O Hilali," commanded the prince.

Abu Zaid said, "I came to your country to take Heesa by stealth. I tricked your people and was taken inside the palace. I would have had the horse anyway. But some evil man had attacked your daughter. In the fight I killed him. So she gave me Heesa as a reward. Thus, she saved the lives of your four slaves and many of your soldiers."

"He lies," cried the vizier.

"No man says that to a Hilali," said Abu Zaid. "Draw your sword."

But the vizier ran from the court. "There will be war," he promised. "Most of the army fights for my money."

"He is right," said the prince.

Already some of the court who were friendly to the vizier were leaving. Civil war was beginning in the realm of Ja'aberie.

"My men and I will fight for you," said Abu Zaid. "Fear not."

The vizier's soldiers attacked the palace that night. Abu Zaid's men had not yet come, and he alone was forced to fight the fight of a hundred men. He held the gate but was badly wounded. He was carried to the chambers, where Alia nursed him.

In the morning the vizier attacked again. His spearmen broke through the first wall, and the soldiers of Ja'aberie had to fall back to the inner walls. The vizier stopped the attack at noon.

"There is no need to fight on in this hot sun," he called. "You are beaten whenever we wish it. I will return this afternoon. I wish to give you and that Hilali dog time to stare at certain defeat and know you can do nothing."

An hour later horsemen appeared at the edge of the town. It was Emir Hassan leading the warriors of Bani Hilal. The army of Hassan drew up in front of the army of the vizier. A challenge went forth from the Hilalies and their leader. The vizier accepted the challenge.

The two heroes, Emir Hassan and the vizier, met as though two mountains had fallen against each other. In the first shock of their meeting their two horses were thrown over. But they remounted and fought on. The din of their swordplay could be heard in the palace. Abu Zaid, listening, said, "That is the ring of a Hilali blade. Soon it will play its music all by itself."

But the vizier fought fiercely. Above the two warriors the bird of destruction stood high in the sky and screamed for joy. Back went the vizier, dodging the blows of Emir Hassan. The vizier's horse backed until his hind legs were cut by the sand and pebbles, but the vizier fought on. He swung a mighty blow with his sword that would have killed any living thing, but Hassan swung under the stomach of his horse and the vizier's sword howled through the empty air. Swinging up from under his horse, Hassan thrust at the vizier and knocked him to the ground. And then Hassan was on him with his dagger in hand.

Before Hassan could deal death with the short blade, the men of the vizier dragged him from the field. Seeing them interfere, the warriors of Bani Hilal charged, and the main battle began. Emir Hassan's horse had been wounded in the fight. He walked about looking for another so that he could lead his men in battle. At that moment Heesa galloped onto the field. She came to Emir Hassan and he mounted her. This time he had no trouble; and, bounding like a gazelle, Heesa jumped over the hedge of long spears that protected the vizier and landed Hassan in the midst of battle.

There Emir Hassan distributed death as generously to his enemies as he distributed food to the poor of Hilal. In the misty din of battle he again sought the vizier, and would have cut through to him if the drums of evening had not begun to sound. Both sides stopped fighting. Emir Hassan's men held the city. The army of the vizier was camped on the plain. Looking out at the tent tops pink with the dying sun, Emir Hassan said, "Tomorrow we will stain them with their blood. Now we must help Abu Zaid."

Without being guided, Heesa took Emir Hassan to the place where Abu Zaid lay wounded.

"In the morning," said Abu Zaid, "give them what they deserve for betraying their prince."

But in the morning the plain was empty. The army of the vizier had run away in the night. Bani Hilal had gained another victory. The kingdom of Ja'aberie was saved.

For many days the Bani Hilal stayed in the city of Ja'aberie feasting, and waiting for Abu Zaid to recover from his wounds. Alia nursed Abu Zaid. On his wounds she put aromatic balm and the finest linens, and soon he was able to join the feast. On the day of the final feast Ja'aberie thanked Abu Zaid.

Abu Zaid rose before all. "I wish to thank the noble Emir Hassan. Without his help I would be dead. I give him now my most priceless gift, the mare Heesa."

All cheered, for no man was more generous than Abu Zaid.

Prince Ja'aberie then rose. "Once I had two priceless possessions. The first was the wonder mare Heesa. Now she belongs to a brave man, Emir Hassan. And now I give my second priceless gift to Abu Zaid. Take my daughter Alia. For her there will be no other but Abu Zaid the Hilali."

Abu Zaid said, "Great has been my gain in this. Long has been my sorrow since my first wife died. Prince Ja'aberie is most generous of all."

The wedding party was formed. A howdaj was made of wood and ivory and covered with green silks and gold. Music makers and dancers moved in front of the howdaj. And for twenty days the way was made merry to the land of the Bani Hilal.

10

THE RETURN OF DIAB

No Arabs took more beautiful women for their wives than the young warriors of Hilal. Zeidan, the younger brother of Hassan, fought his way to Hindustan to take Princess Samia as his wife. Mukhiebar, son of Abu Zaid, bested all rivals and wed the beauty, Princess Sa'ad el Raja. Murshid, son of Diab ben Gannim, killed a jinni to win Reema. The old Hilalies, seeing the young warriors return with their brides, were happy for them and proud of the tribe.

"These are fine years," said the old warriors. "The Bani Hilal will not die as long as young men of spirit are born to us."

When Diab's son returned to the station at Saroo with the beautiful Reema, the old warriors shook the earth with the butts of their lances. "A fine sight," said the scarred sword-bearer of Hassan. "Oh that his father were here to see him. Diab would be proud of his son."

All were happy for Murshid, but sad because Diab, his father, still wandered the wilderness, away from his people. Because they felt sorrow for Murshid and Diab, the warriors of Hilal each gave two camels and one sheep for the wedding feast of Reema. So the son of Diab, though his father was not with the tribe, had the greatest feast of all. A thousand camels were given for the wedding. After the feasting and the games, Jazieh, sister of Hassan, sang a sad poem about Diab.

"Sing a happier song for happier times," ordered Emir Hassan, who was greatly touched at the sad memory of Diab.

Jazieh, who was there visiting her tribesmen, sang of the brave deeds of the young warriors of Hilal. She sang of the long, hard journey into Hindustan where Zeidan won Samia. She sang of the rivals overthrown by Mukhiebar as he won Sa'ad el Raja. She sang of the fight between Murshid and the jinni of Jabal al-Burj. And she sang of Yaya who left the tents of the Bani Hilal in secret, telling no one the name of the woman of his quest. Yaya had been killed by fierce warriors in the north, his body torn apart, and only his sword returned to Bani Hilal. Jazieh sang of Yaya and his beloved whose name was known only to the highest God. Jazieh also sang of a five-year war that began when Merieme had been kidnaped by a young man of the tribe. She sang of all heroes and their women.

Jabir, son of Hassan, listened to the songs of his aunt and the cheers of the Hilalies when the names of heroes and their ladies were praised. Jabir was only sixteen, but he had done many brave things. Yet Jazieh did not mention him. When the song was done, Jabir went to his aunt. "Aunt," he said, "you sang of everyone's valor but mine. But you said nothing of my noble deeds."

The beautiful Jazieh laughed at her nephew who only a few years before had sat on her knee in the tents. "You should stay in your mother's tent longer, my chick. Soon enough you will be fit to be sung of as a man."

Jabir flew into a great rage when his beautiful aunt laughed at him. He drew his sword and shook it in the air. "If I must unsheathe my sword to be counted great, then let it be so!" he shouted. "Tell me of the most beautiful woman of all. I will take her though I must cut a way through armies with this sword."

"Forgive me," said Jazieh. "I see that you are determined to be greatest of the tribe. You are then in truth the man fit to marry Badre el Na'am who dwells in a palace beyond the Great Wilderness."

"Sing to me of Badre el Na'am," Jabir begged his aunt.

"I will sing of her," said Jazieh. "But once you hear, you will leave for her tents and never rest until you have her as your wife."

Jazieh drew off her veil, and with her lovely face in shadow and only her throat white against the moonlight, she sang, "Badre el Na'am's veil is stirred in the night wind. It falls aside. And behold, there is her face, and the moon hides behind a dark cloud in envy. And what of men? None look at her. They cannot. For they have all thrown themselves on the ground to worship at her feet.

"Once I had a beautiful white bird. It was given to me by Diab because I was the fairest of all Arab women. But one day the white bird flew away to the west. All of our warriors searched for it. But no one found it. Then the word came to us that the bird had flown to the land of Badre el Na'am. A messenger came to us, saying, 'What good will it do to bring the bird back here? It will only fly away to Badre el Na'am again. For the bird will stay with the fairest woman of the Arabs. And the fairest one of all is Badre.' Though the man was seized and though they threatened to cut out his tongue unless he swore that I, Jazieh, was the fairest Arab woman, he would not. So a poet of our tribe traveled to the land of Badre el Na'am to see if the man spoke the truth. And he did. She is fairer. And the bird remains with her. Bring her to the land of the Hilalies and the white bird follows."

"Sing no more," said Jabir. "I will leave the Nejd this night. I will be the one man to look on her beauty. For I will be her husband."

Jabir prepared the fastest horse of his father's stable, and rode off into the moonlight. For three days Jabir rode up towering white dunes. From the dune tops he looked over the desert sea before he let his horse slide down the sand mountains. On the third day, Jabir saw on a distant dune an Arab rider who was spying out the country like himself. I will capture him, thought Jabir, and this search will begin with a brave deed. Jabir took his horse down into a twisting *wadi* and rode toward where the rider had been. Before he reached the spot, Jabir left his horse and, carrying his sword, crept up the side of the dune. Working around the edge of the dune, Jabir raised his sword and made ready to charge. But a voice behind him called out, "Jabir, son of Hassan. What are you doing in this enemy country?"

It was Akrama, youngest son of Abu Zaid. Jabir told his friend of his vow to seek Badre el Na'am.

"Friend," said Akrama, "I will not forsake you, but rather go with you. For the road is hard ahead. One alone can do nothing."

So the two friends traveled on into enemy country. On the fifth day they saw a rider approaching, and they waited for him in the shadow of a sand hill. But when the rider galloped near them, they saw that it was Mahmoud, the second son of Diab ben Gannim.

"You here too, Mahmoud," they called to their friend. "What beauty do you seek?"

"I seek no beauty," said Mahmoud. "I seek a noble man with a full beard, my father, the mighty Diab ben Gannim. He has been long forgiven by your fathers. And still he wanders in the wilderness. For this reason I seek him. Until he returns I cannot think of a fair bride."

"Perhaps we can do all these things together," said Akrama. "The land of Badre el Na'am lies beyond the Great Wilderness.

As we pass through the wilderness or on our return we may hear of your mighty father. Will you join us?"

"I will go anywhere that will bring me near my father," answered Mahmoud.

The three friends pressed on toward the edge of the Great Wilderness. As they neared it, the acacia and thorn grew thicker; the sand ended and rocks of fierce and wild shapes blocked their path. They traveled along the edge of the Great Wilderness. There the thorn had wrapped itself so tightly about the rocks that it made a wall. The horses could not pass through the wall of thorn and rock. They searched for an entrance. As they searched they heard the sound of horses crashing through the thicket. They hid behind a rock and waited. But no enemy soldiers came out of the Great Wilderness, only a small merchant, Ibrahim, who was of a tribe friendly to Bani Hilal.

They greeted Ibrahim, and he replied, "Peace. What are you young men doing here on the edge of the Great Wilderness?"

"We seek the land of Badre el Na'am which is beyond the wilderness," said Jabir. "But we can find no path. How did you get through, Ibrahim?"

"Ah, the path is hard," Ibrahim told them. "Only this one camel knows the way through the thickets. I send her ahead and follow her. She leads the rest of my horses and camels. Otherwise, I would become lost in the dark places in there."

"Sell us this camel," begged Jabir. "We will give you one thousand dinars for your wise camel."

Ibrahim did not wish to sell his camel, but the price was great and he was a merchant, who had to talk money to keep breath-ing. "I will take two thousand," he said.

After much talk they agreed to pay fifteen hundred dinars. Each boy wrote a paper that his father would pay five hundred.

"But how do I know I will collect the price from Diab?" asked the merchant.

"We will find him," said Mahmoud. "He is in the wilderness. My father will pay you."

Ibrahim said, "Then I must ask two thousand, a thousand from Diab and five hundred each from Emir Hassan and Abu

Zaid. It may take you years to find Diab. If I take such risk I must have the chance of gain."

As Ibrahim took the papers and began to lead his camels and horses away, he said, "I will ask your families to say the prayers of the dead for you, because I doubt that you will come from the Great Wilderness alive. Peace be on you." The three young men followed Ibraham's camel into the dark thicket of the Great Wilderness. The country of Badre el Na'am lay beyond the thicket, and Jabir urged the camel forward with a stick.

As Jabir, Akrama, and Mahmoud slowly worked their way through the wilderness, desperate events were taking place in the country of Badre el Na'am. For many years Badre's father, King Nehrad, had been paying heavy tribute to the powerful King of Sour. Each year the demands of this wicked king increased. Now a rider from the King of Sour came to the palace of King Nehrad.

"What are the demands of your greedy master this time?" asked King Nehrad.

"One tenth of all money earned, grain grown, and cattle raised in your kingdom last year," said the messenger.

"Very well," said King Nehrad, with a sigh. "But the price is heavy."

"The price is even heavier," the messenger replied. "The King of Sour also wants the pick of fifty of your most beautiful girls to be wed to his bravest soldiers."

"Oh," exclaimed King Nehrad, "I will never be able to face my soldiers with that request. What will they think of me?"

"They will have sympathy for you," said the messenger, "when they learn that our king wants your daughter Badre el Na'am as his wife. Go now and tell them."

King Nehrad gathered his warriors in the palace yard. "I must tell you of the demands of the King of Sour," he announced. "They are heavy. First he wishes one tenth of all money earned, grain grown, and cattle raised."

The soldiers groaned.

"Then he asks for fifty of our fairest girls for his bravest soldiers."

The soldiers began to murmur angrily.

"Lastly, he asks for Badre el Na'am as his wife."

A great roar came from every soldier. "Never!" they shouted. "We will fight to the death."

So King Nehrad and his soldiers prepared for war. The messenger was sent back to Sour with sand stuffed in his mouth, and with the message: "We give you only this in tribute."

The King of Sour marched against King Nehrad. From the walls of his castle Nehrad watched the hosts of Sour moving across the plain. The line of battle ran from one side of the plain to the other. The depth of the moving lines was so great that Nehrad could not see the last rank. The armies of Sour rolled on like the sea, and the earth was chewed to bits by the feet of horses and men. The army, chanting and clashing their swords, gave off a frightful din that echoed across the plain and beat against the walls of the castle.

Nehrad ordered all of the women and the young and the very old to be taken far into the castle and placed behind the thickest stones of the inner fortress. If the outer walls fell, the army would press back against the last wall and die fighting to protect the women. If the last wall were broken, archers would fire down among the women, killing them all before they were seized by the armies of Sour. King Nehrad then led his army out against Sour. The two forces met in the middle of the plain.

When Jabir, Akrama, and Mahmoud came to the back walls

of the castle from the depths of the Great Wilderness, they saw no one moving on the ramparts. "Can this be the castle of Badre el Na'am?" asked Akrama. "The place seems deserted. On all the ramparts I see not one guard."

"True," agreed Mahmoud. "And in all these lush meadows not one sheep grazes. The castle is empty or enchanted. Let us pass on."

"There are people in the castle," Jabir said. "And my heart's voice tells me that Badre el Na'am is one of them. Let us go inside the walls. Perhaps they need help here."

At that moment a maid walked out of the castle, ran to a spring and filled her water jug. As she ran back to the small gate, Jabir stopped her. "Where are the owners of the castle?" he asked.

But the maid could answer not a word. She began to scream and cry. She dropped her water jug and tried to run for the gate. But Jabir held her. "Be not afraid," he said. "We are not enemies of your people."

The maid, weeping, told him about the attack by the King of Sour.

The three young men drew their swords. "We came to fight for Badre el Na'am," said Jabir. "But if your king needs our help against such a wicked man, we offer help gladly. We will fight for Badre el Na'am later."

"You do both," said the maid. "For this is the castle of Badre el Na'am." She led the three men into the inner castle where the women were. "We will stand here," decided Jabre.

"If the forces of Sour break through the first line, we will make them pay heavily."

From beyond the front walls of the castle came the sound of battle. As they waited for the enemy to appear or for the forces of Nehrad to conquer, a beautiful woman came out of the inner walls. Seeing her, Jabir cried to his companions, "Oh, such beauty. Never have I seen its like."

"Do not forget you are sworn to love Badre el Na'am," Mahmoud reminded him.

"If this girl is Badre, well I love her," said Jabir. "But if not, then this is my bride-to-be. Never has beauty so moved me on one single sight."

The beautiful girl approached the three warriors of Hilal. "What brave people are these who fight for us?" she asked them.

Jabir said, "We are the Hilalies — Jabir, Akrama, and Mahmoud, sons of Hassan, Abu Zaid, and Diab. And for one as beautiful as you we would die in this place a thousand times if we had that many lives. Tell us the name of the woman we are ready to die for?"

"I am Badre el Na'am," she said. "This is the castle of my father Nehrad."

"Then we are not dying in the wrong place," said Jabir. "I come from the Nejd seeking you. I wish to take you as a bride to the Bani Hilal."

"First you must save me," said Badre, "and three men cannot do that. It seems I will be your bride of death."

As she spoke a great shout arose from the front of the walls. The army of Nehrad was falling back before the King of Sour. "Already it is too late," cried Badre. "The forces of Sour are under the first walls."

Drawing his sword, Jabir led Akrama and Mahmoud to the walls. From the walls the three Hilalies jumped into the battle. So vast a path did they cut in the ranks of the soldiers of Sour that the enemy fell back on all sides. Jabir was a raging tiger. He struck down soldiers with the fore swing of his sword and cleared another path with the back swing. Mahmoud with his great strength hurled three soldiers from the walls, and enemy were knocked backward as though a mountain had rolled down on them. Akrama hurled javelin after javelin, never missing, and sometimes pinning two riders with a single cast. So fought the three young men of Bani Hilal, while the forces of Nehrad rallied and gained strength and finally attacked again. A new battle raged with the Hilalies cutting a path for the others to follow.

When evening came the drums boomed from the walls and from out on the plain. The two armies stopped fighting. Not even the first wall had been taken. Nehrad invited the three Hilalies to a feast in the castle.

"How is it?" he asked, "that three strangers of the Nejd come to this land to serve me? You are truly friends."

"Then friends should not lie to each other," said Jabir. "I came to ask for your daughter Badre as my wife. But if she had not been given, I planned to take her. These, my friends Akrama and Mahmoud, came to help me."

"You need not take her," said Nehrad. "She is yours as a reward for bravery. Now you must only save her from the King of Sour. The battle went against us today. Without you, the walls would have gone to the enemy. I am too old and weak to fight. I have no young strong son. Only Badre."

"Through Badre you have a son," cried Jabir. "A son as true as your promise that she is to be my wife. Better than one son you have three, because my friends will fight beside me."

Akrama and Mahmoud nodded.

"I have this day depended on your strong arms and keen

blade," said King Nehrad. "But the Hilalies are famed for wit as well as strength. What is your advice?"

"Ask Akrama," said Jabir. "He is the best at advising, for his father is Abu Zaid the Hilali, greatest of warriors and advisers on war. How do you advise, Akrama?"

"We must send for our fathers and the swiftest and strongest *gom* of the Bani Hilal," said Akrama. "Since we are their sons, they will send help."

"But how can we send a messenger?" asked Nehrad. "There is no time even for the swiftest rider. Only a bird could fly to the Nejd in time."

"There is a bird that knows the way," said Badre el Na'am. "It is the Bird of Beauty. Once it was with Jazieh, sister of Emir Hassan. But then it flew to me here."

"Because you were more beautiful," said Jabir.

"True," replied Badre. "But if I should lose my beauty, the bird would return at once to Jazieh and we could send a message with it. It would fly over the Great Wilderness swiftly."

Saying this, Badre el Na'am seized a torch from the wall and would have thrust the fire against her face, but Jabir stopped her.

"If we must die, then we will," said Jabir. "But never will I permit that beauty to be destroyed."

"What does one face matter when the lives of all are threatened?" asked Badre. "You cannot stop me. After I retire I will disfigure my face. Then the bird will fly. Prepare the message."

"I cannot let you do that," said Jabir. "I will guard you."

Through the night Jabir guarded Badre el Na'am, never allowing her to leave the narrow, empty chamber in which she slept. Toward dawn Mahmoud was supposed to relieve Jabir and keep a watch until daybreak. But Mahmoud never appeared. Jabir fought against sleep. He could not sit or he drowsed. He could not stand or he drowsed. Fatigued from his long journey and a day of battle, his bones aching, and his head swimming with fatigue, he marched up and down the corridor during the long night. Finally he could walk no further without supporting himself with his hands against the stone walls. And there against the cool stone walls he finally fell, rolled to the floor and slept a deep sleep. Still Mahmoud did not come.

All through the night Badre el Na'am waited behind the door of her chamber. She listened to the footsteps of Jabir. She heard them falter, stop, and then begin again. Many times she opened the door just a little to see if her lover slept. But stumbling and falling Jabir kept going until the walls of the chamber bore a thin saffron bar from the first light. Then he fell and slept.

Badre el Na'am crept from her room. She hurried along the corridor toward the niche in the inner wall where she had hidden a knife in case the forces of Sour broke through. She had planned to destroy herself if her own archers did not kill her. Now she planned only to destroy her great beauty.

Already her maid had prepared a message to be tied to the leg of the Bird of Beauty. The message would bring the warriors of Bani Hilal and save all of her people, but most important

Jabir would be saved. Probably, she thought, he will never marry me when I am no longer beautiful. But at least he will live. That is joy enough for me.

Badre reached the inner wall. She placed her hand into a gap in the stones. The knife was there! She removed her veil and drew forth the cold blade.

But before she could slash at her face, two horsemen burst in through the back gate. There was light enough to see that one was Mahmoud. The other was a big man who rode a wondrous mare. The man looked much like Mahmoud. She knew then that she gazed on the mighty Diab ben Gannim and his mare Khadra.

The horsemen galloped toward her. Diab stopped his mare and she reared high and pawed in the air and called the fierce trumpet of a war horse.

"Quickly," shouted Diab to Mahmoud. "Get grain for Khadra and then ride for the Bani Hilal. Only Khadra can bear you to them in time. But you must ride her. I will stay, and with Akrama and Jabir, I will hold the walls until help comes. Go."

Mahmoud did not argue with his father. He picked up a sack of grain, leaped on Khadra, and flew out of the gates.

Diab then approached Badre el Na'am, who had stood looking at the great warrior in silent awe. "This is a fierce city," Diab said, "when beauties like you carry short blades. Give me that."

He took the knife from Badre el Na'am. "Last night my son

Mahmoud found me in the Great Wilderness," said he. "These walls will stand until help comes if I must support them with only my own shoulders."

The walls stood. Diab raged and fought away all soldiers of Sour who dared approach him, and the soldiers of King Nehrad took courage from Diab's leadership and fought brilliantly behind him. In a shorter time than anyone believed possible — because the great mare Khadra had carried the message for help — the first forces of Bani Hilal arrived and swept the army of Sour across the plain.

"Victory is ours!" cried King Nehrad. "The Bani Hilal have saved us."

But the battle was not over. The treacherous King of Sour sent some of his men to raid the camp of the Bani Hilal. There were few warriors at camp to stand against the enemy. The women and children of Bani Hilal would have perished, except for Diab and Emir Hassan. Hearing that their station had been attacked roused the Hilalies to fury, and they cut down the half of the army of Sour that opposed them. But their tents and families were threatened by Sour's other forces, and there was no time for all of the warriors to ride to Saroo. Only the two swiftest horses could get there in time. Diab started on Khadra and Emir Hassan started on Heesa. The two horses flew through the night like dark birds and arrived in the Nejd in the morning.

Though Khadra was like the wind, Heesa was like lightning in a night sky, and Emir Hassan was the first to reach the station, though Diab was only a breath behind him. In the first contest then, Heesa had beaten Khadra. Diab and Emir Hassan rallied a few old warriors and charged the forces of Sour. Diab himself killed the King of Sour and his army turned and fled.

Afterwards, King Nehrad ruled over his own land and the land of Sour. The people were glad to live under a wise and generous king. A great feast was held when Jabir married Badre el Na'am. Flutes played, the girls danced to the *dubkeh,* and the Bird of Beauty hovered overhead.

On the hillside above the wedding place, sat Emir Hassan with Diab on his left and Abu Zaid on his right.

"When the horse games begin," said Diab, "my Khadra will be ready to race Heesa."

"Heesa has once beaten your Khadra," Emir Hassan reminded him.

"That race was unequal," said Diab. "Khadra had flown the course twice."

"Peace," said Abu Zaid. "Peace be among the Hilalies. The old ones should watch and be silent and have joy in their hearts for the good fortune of the young."

Heeding the wise Abu Zaid, Diab and Hassan were silent; for the day did truly belong to the young and the fair.

11

A BLESSING AND A CURSE

And the word went out to all the Faithful of the Nejd that they were needed by the Prophet Mohammed, the true Apostle of God. The Prophet had decreed that the sword must be carried against the Bani Fana, who worshipped many false gods. To make the Fana worship the one true God, the Faithful rallied to the call of the Prophet, and the great battle began.

Now the Bani Fana were as many as the waves in the sea, the sands of the desert, and the leaves of the trees. Though the Faithful fought with zeal, they could not break through the whirlwind charge of the Bani Fana. And truly it was a whirlwind. The Bani Fana fought in this way: So many were their horses and men that when they attacked they rode in a great circle, riding in and out, and swirling around until their dust towered into the heavens. Fana riders on the outside rode steadily in toward the center. Those in the inside rode toward the outer circle. So they moved swirling and sweeping all enemy horsemen into their center. It was like a great wind or the devil's whirlpool in the sea. Horses and men sucked into the center were lost forever. In the center, a hundred giant Nubians with huge blades cut enemy soldiers from their horses.

The Fana army was a whirlwind, a whirlpool, a monster. Against such devils only one could stand — Mohammed, the true Prophet. And so he and the tribes of the Faithful rode out to meet the whirlwind.

The forces of the Faithful were drawn up on the mountainside of Jabal al-Soda (Black Mountain). Across the Plain of al-Ashrar (Plain of the Bad) rolled the host of the Fana. Dust stood high in the sky. The sun was blotted out. It was dark in the day, and only the Prophet could see into the ranks of the Fana.

"They are many," cried the Faithful. "Hundreds. Thousands. Who can stand against them?"

There was fear among the Faithful.

Under the calm eyes of the Prophet, the fear that ran along the line of the Faithful was soon gone. The Faithful calmed their camels and horses and watched the whirlwind come out of the plain.

"*Ya Hai!*" cried the Faithful. They moved back against the hill, ready to run away.

But one brave man raised himself on his horse. Standing in

his stirrups he bore witness in such a voice that it was heard by all of the Faithful.

"*La Illaha, Illa' Allah* . . ." He waved his arm toward the Fana. "*Allah Akbar*. Onward!"

Horses cried. Camels screamed. He spurred his horse onto the plain. And the Faithful charged toward the enemy.

But the Faithful could not break the swirling wall of the Fana. Great ones disappeared into the awful whirling depths of the enemy. So died Hazan Abu Ibrahim, Umar and many of the great and good — May God hold them in His favor. The Prophet, fearing for the lives of the Faithful that remained, had the drums beaten for retreat. Few were the Faithful that came back to the hillside of Jabal al-Soda. From the hill, the Prophet wept as he saw the Faithful down on the plain sucked into the center of the Fana hordes. There they would die. Fatima, favorite daughter of Mohammed, galloped close to her father.

"Can nothing be done?" she cried. "Must they die?"

The Prophet shook his head and gave no answer. Already, many of the Faithful had been drawn into the center of the swirling cloud of the Fana. Already, many valiant sons were dead. Happily they were in Paradise, but the rest of the Faithful were still in danger. The Fana drew off into the middle of the Plain of al-Ashrar to finish their victims. There they continued to send dust high into the air with their crazed dancing and riding.

From the hillside, the Faithful watched. Some waited without a word. Some beat their breasts, tore their clothes and wailed, "How can we stand against monsters who take the form of a whirlwind? Man cannot fight the wind. The sons of the Faithful need the help of Allah."

All eyes were on Mohammed who sat his camel and stared toward the Holy Place. He waited a sign from God. Would it come? the soldiers wondered. Mohammed rode his camel forward.

"See if any among the Fana will come out and face our heroes in single combat," he ordered.

Horsemen from the Faithful rode out with the challenge. By the rules, any army had first to send heroes out to fight in single combat. But the Fana were not humans. They were the sons of the evil wind. They were sand devils.

The Fana mocked the horsemen who came out from the Faithful. "All must die," they cried. "This is not boys' work we do here. This is no game."

With that, the whirlwind moved slowly toward the Faithful horsemen. Drums beat a warning from the hillside. And the horsemen galloped back.

Now it was clear why the Fana had not attacked the Faithful on the hillside. The Fana horses and camels were trained for the flat, open plain. On the plain, the Fana could ride in their great, swirling circle. This they could not do on the hillside. There the ground was broken with deep gulleys and strewn with heavy boulders. No cavalry could keep the simplest formation on such rough ground.

For the moment the Faithful were safe. The Fana would not attack them on the rugged slopes of Jabal al-Soda. Nor would the Fana send their heroes in single combat against the heroes of the Faithful. In the ranks of the Faithful were great swords such as Ali Ibn al-Aqsa, men skilled with the javelin, as Abd al-Aziz, and the mighty al-Asadi. No, the Fana were cowards. They could fight only in a mob where their devilish cavalry would devour the Faithful. Most of the Faithful were mounted on camels, or afoot. Swift horsemen were needed to ride against the Fana.

The Fana waited in the plain. They prowled around like wild beasts, swirling in and out, throwing dust up to the heaven, an offence in the eyes of God. They would not come to the Jabal al-Soda. But the Faithful could not come down from the hill. The Fana had surrounded the hill on all sides. If the Faithful rode away they would be cut down to a man.

The Prophet Mohammed rode to the highest point of the mountain, and prepared to say his prayers of the evening. Some of the soldiers feared that the Faithful would never look into the reddening sky of another evening. As the clear call of the prayer came down the mountainside all the Faithful took heart. All prayed.

As the sound of prayer whispered away, out in the haze of the plain another great cloud of dust appeared. A horde of horsemen rode out of the western sun and across the plain. Faster they came. The dying sun lived again, dancing on ten thousand drawn swords. The thunder of horses' hoofs filled the plain and drowned even the sound of the restless prowling Fana. Above all, came a cry sweet to the ears of the Faithful.

"Bani Hilal! Bani Hilal! We ride to serve a Prophet who is true. The Sons of Hilal come with ten thousand swords."

The Fana turned their swirling circle to meet the Hilal horsemen. There was the sound of a mountain falling or heaven splitting as the two armies met in head-on course. Dust blotted out all sight. Bedouin cries, the terror of horses, and the triumphant cries of men filled the Plain of al-Ashrar.

Mohammed was already mounted. "Forward," he cried. "For Allah! Allah is great!"

Down the slope charged the Faithful. Even Fatima, the Prophet's favorite daughter, drove her camel toward the fight. The Hilal, hitting from the west, split through to the center of the Fana whirlwind. Hitting from the east, the Faithful broke the outer circle and drove in on the Nubian swordsmen. In the center, the slaughter was great. The monster was pierced to his heart. The great circle had been broken. Hilalies and the

Faithful joined forces there. The plain was a forest swept by a great fire wind. The Fana were broken.

It was nearly dark when Mohammed and the Faithful pulled back to the hillside of Jabal al-Soda. There the ranks were formed, the wounded treated, and the dead buried. Prayers were said.

All was not joy. Many were dead, dying, or missing. In the fight, the daughter of the Prophet, Fatima herself, was gone because her camel had charged ahead of her bodyguard. Mohammed, sorrowing, sent soldiers to search through the dead on the plain.

"Now bring the chiefs of the Bani Hilal before me," Mohammed commanded.

Emir Hassan, Abu Zaid, Diab ben Gannim, and other great Hilali warriors stood before the Prophet.

"Your work served Allah and the Faithful," Mohammed said. "Henceforth the tribe of Hilal will ride with the Faithful. The work of bringing the true God to the rest of the world will be partly yours. I bless you." The Hilali chiefs stood down from their horses to receive the blessing.

"May you always be victorious," the Prophet Mohammed said. "From this day on may the name of Hilal be blessed."

"And I curse them!" cried a voice from the darkness.

Out of the shadows came a wild-eyed woman, and it was none other than the favored Fatima herself. It was she who called the curse on the Bani Hilal, and it was later known that she did so because she blamed the Hilalies for nearly causing

her death. In the fight, a wild warrior of the Bani Hilal, thinking only of battle and wanting to get the woman out of his way,
had slashed her camel and caused it to bolt. She had been
dragged across the plain and left hanging in a bush. She had
only now made her way back up the Jabal al-Soda.

Her eyes blazed as she walked toward the Hilali chiefs.
"Curse the Bani Hilal," she said. "May they be scattered to
the four winds."

Mohammed tried to quiet her, but it was too late. A curse
from the mouth of the daughter of the Prophet had been
spoken, and once spoken, it could not be undone, even by Mohammed himself. Though the Bani Hilal had received a great
blessing from the Prophet himself, they had also received a
great curse to bear with it.

And so the fate of the Sons of Hilal had been spoken, and
it came to pass in that way. The greatness of the Emir Hassan,
Abu Zaid, Diab ben Gannim, and their sons and son's sons led
the Bani Hilal to victory after victory through the years. But
always they moved across the land, and finally into Africa,
seeking the well that was not dry, the ground that was not
parched, the hill that had grass for sheep and goats.

No tribe was as great as the Bani Hilal, but with the four
winds they drifted.

A Glossary of Terms

Aadite   — kind of armor

Bani   — sons of, tribe of

Bedouin or Badu — Arab who lives or wanders in the desert

Cut sand   — Arab method of seeing into the future

Dervish   — wandering holy man

Dinar   — Arab coin

Dubkeh   — dance of ancient Arabia

Durbukeh   — drum of ancient Arabia

Emir   — Arab ruler

Falchion   — curved sword

Gom   — raiding party

Hijaz   — kingdom of Arabia

Hilali   — tribesman of Hilal

Howdaj   — riding platform on a camel

Islam	— Moslem world
Jabal	— mountain
Jinni, also Genie	— spirit or monster, usually wicked
Mecca	— city and kingdom of ancient Arabia
Mehari	— a breed of desert camels
Mohammed	— Prophet who brought Moslem religion to Arabs
Moslem	— follower of religion founded by Mohammed
Nejd	— province or kingdom of ancient Arabia
Nijmeh	— star
Nukut	— gifts to honor a newborn son
Rasad	— a monster guardian
Roum	— kingdom of Middle East
Scimiter	— curved sword
Sheikh	— Arab leader
Shereff	— nobleman of Arabia
Tahamah	— kingdom of Arabia
Vizier	— adviser to a king
Wadi	— stream beds or narrow valleys
Yemen	— kingdom of ancient Arabia